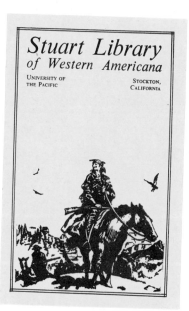

Books by Floyd Miller

THE SAVAGE STREETS

THE DREAM PEDDLERS

JUST SO FAR

SCANDALE

BEYOND MY WORTH (*with Lillian Roth*)

THE KIND OF GUY I AM (*with Robert McAllister*)

THE ORDERLY DISORDERLY HOUSE (*with Carol Erwin*)

THE MAN WHO SOLD THE EIFFEL TOWER (*with James Johnson*)

THE ELECTRICAL GENIUS OF LIBERTY HALL

AHDOOLO

WILD CHILDREN OF THE URALS

BILL TILGHMAN

BILL TILGHMAN

Floyd Miller

BILL TILGHMAN

MARSHAL OF THE LAST FRONTIER

Doubleday & Company, Inc.

Garden City, New York

1968

For that tiny enchantress—
Jennifer

ACKNOWLEDGMENTS

You can take the girl out of Oklahoma but not Oklahoma out of the girl. Carol Lynn Gilmer was an associate editor of *Reader's Digest* in New York yet she maintained that the sun was brighter, the rain fresher, the grass sweeter, the people friendlier, the crimes bloodier back home in Oklahoma. Her hero was Bill Tilghman, U. S. Marshal for Oklahoma Territory in the land run days after the Civil War, and she engaged in a long campaign to get his story written.

Carol Lynn was not only the inspiration for this book but when I made my first research trip to Oklahoma she provided a wise counselor—her father, Tom Gilmer, then Mayor of Okmulgee.

Oklahomans are engaging people, but none more so than James Slack of the Amerada Petroleum Corporation in Tulsa. He not only made available his company's records and photographs of Oklahoma's early oil boom days, but he fed my wife and me home-cooked ribs, and introduced us to the excitement of being "rock hounds."

The present lawmen of Oklahoma are hardly more than a generation away from the frontier days; not far enough to have lost the traditional independence and courage, pride in their star. Among such men who shared their stories with me were Joe Hagen, former Sheriff of Slick and Cromwell;

William Nicholson, Sheriff of Wewoka; John ("Uncle Bill") Cross, eighty-four-year-old bailiff and constable in Wewoka; and Lloyd Fullerlove, constable in Chandler.

The newspapermen who were generous with their material were Dick Miller, author of "The Smoking Room" appearing in *The Oklahoman & Times;* Virgil Curry, librarian, *Tulsa World* and *Tribune;* and Russel Gideon, editor, Sunday Supplement, *Tulsa World.*

Joe Looney, Wewoka lawyer, politician and civic leader, supplied many documents pertaining to Tilghman's last violent days. Homer Bishop, a prosecutor in the Wiley Lynn murder trial, still practices law in Seminole and spent an afternoon explaining to me the facts behind that miscarriage of justice.

Zoe Tilghman, William Tilghman's widow, was of the greatest assistance, making available to me not only her written works but her personal reminiscences. Between the time I interviewed her and the publication of this book, she died. She was a gallant lady.

Gracious and helpful was her son, Tench Tilghman; her stepchildren, Charles and Dorothy Tilghman; and her step-grandson, Charles Tilghman, Jr.

The most extensive collection of Great Plains Americana I know of is the Frank Phillips Collection in the University of Oklahoma Library in Norman. Dr. A. M. Gibson, the Curator, guided my research in his department and generously supplied the pictures that appear in this book. He also made available the assistance of two extremely knowledgeable archivists, Mrs. Boyce Timmons and Vynola Newkumet.

My wife, Meg, shared the burdens of research and observed the unfolding story with infectious enthusiasm.

LIST OF ILLUSTRATIONS

1. Flora Kendall Tilghman, Tilghman's romantic first love, was embittered by the demands of his profession. (University of Oklahoma)
2. Zoe Stratton Tilghman, Tilghman's mettlesome second wife, could write poetry as well as she roped calves. (University of Oklahoma)
3. The start of the famous run of homesteaders into the Cherokee Strip, Indian Territory, in 1893. (University of Oklahoma)
4. This bleak half-dugout was typical of the primitive dwellings of early settlers in Oklahoma. (University of Oklahoma)
5. The sod house was the homesteader's solution to the problem of building material on Oklahoma's treeless plains. (University of Oklahoma)
6. Company H, 13th Infantry, U.S. troops stationed on Cottonwood Creek near Guthrie in Indian Territory in 1889. (University of Oklahoma)
7. The Merchant's Bank, first bank in Guthrie, was organized overnight by self-constituted bankers. (University of Oklahoma)
8. A mob around the Guthrie jail in 1889. Pioneer tempers were short and justice was apt to be swift. (University of Oklahoma)

BILL TILGHMAN

I

Four men dressed in business suits and dusty boots stood outside of town and waited. They spoke little but their anxieties were revealed by the way they frequently squinted down the rutted road that ran west out of town and across the August-parched plains of Oklahoma.

William Sirmans, secretary of the Chamber of Commerce and leader of this small group which called itself "Cromwell Citizens for Law and Order," took a large gold watch from his pocket and studied it.

"He's late?" one of the men asked. "Maybe he won't come."

Sirmans returned the watch to his pocket and said, "No, he's not late. We're early. And he'll come."

"What if he doesn't?"

"He will," Sirmans insisted.

"I'm just saying what *if* . . . what *if*. Well, I can tell you what *I'm* gonna do if he doesn't come. I'm leaving town."

"On a fence rail?" one of the men cracked.

It was a poor joke, under the circumstances, and no one laughed. These men, all merchants in the oil boom town of Cromwell, Oklahoma, had petitioned Governor Martin E. Trapp to send them a man to clean up their town, make it safe to live in. If the Governor now failed them they might well have to leave their homes and businesses. A new type of criminal had descended on the Oklahoma boom towns during this year of 1924; men who had never ridden a horse, city men who wore loud suits and pointed shoes and sold bootleg whiskey and women. To protect their profits they had to control the town—bribing where possible, killing when necessary. Governor Trapp had promised to send to Cromwell a lawman who could withstand both bribery and terrorism, a man who had become a legend in his time—William Matthew Tilghman.

Tilghman had grown up with the West; had been a buffalo hunter, Indian fighter, cowboy, horse breeder, rancher, sheriff, United States Marshal, State Senator, special deputy for President Theodore Roosevelt. He was now seventy years old and had given up his retirement only at the greatest urging.

"That must be him!" one of the committee shouted, pointing to a plume of dust that marked the teetering approach of a high-wheeled Model T Ford. The car braked to a shuddering stop and Bill Tilghman climbed out to meet the committee. Except for Sirmans, who knew him, the committeemen were disappointed in what they saw. Instead of a man of steely fierceness they shook hands with a man who was soft-spoken, seemed almost gentle. He was immaculately groomed and wore a carefully knotted necktie with a gold nugget stickpin. His expensive ten-gallon hat of creamy whiteness was tall and uncreased, and on his square, lined face there was a handlebar mustache. In this era of bathtub gin and flappers, everything about him seemed slightly old-fashioned. He looked like a favorite grandfather, tolerant and wise and a giver of gifts. The Citizens Committee was dismayed at the thought of this gentle old man facing the crooks and degenerates that infested Cromwell.

After the formalities of the introductions, Tilghman began to ask questions: What was the pattern of crime in Cromwell? How many assaults? Rapes? Thefts? Murders? What was the bootleggers' source of supply? Were there narcotics in town? How much prostitution?

Tilghman's voice took on a note of command and he no longer seemed old-fashioned—he was a professional going about a job he understood.

"Mr. Tilghman, we just don't know a lot of the answers," Sirmans finally said. He gestured toward the town. "Five months ago there was one cabin there. Oil was found and now we got ten or fifteen thousand people, more coming all the time. Every sheriff we've had was bought out or run out."

"How about the district attorney?" Tilghman asked.

"Can't count on him. The county judge is in Wewoka, George Crump is his name, and he's a good man. It's best to take any prisoners to Wewoka."

Tilghman asked, "If I have to deputize a posse, who can I count on?"

There was a pause while Sirmans exchanged glances with the other three men of his committee. Finally, with an apologetic smile, he said, "Us."

Tilghman nodded matter-of-factly.

"If you succeed in getting some of the crooks convicted and sent to jail, other men will come forward," Sirmans said, "but right now all you can count on is us."

"Very good. Now, where is my office and my jail?"

"We'll escort you there, Marshal."

"Thank you, no. When a man has fewer troops than the enemy, it's better not to display them at all. I'll go alone." With one foot on the running board he said, "Who's the top dog?"

"You mean a gang leader, a boss? I don't think there is any. Things are too wild and disorganized in Cromwell to have a leader."

"If there isn't one now, there soon will be. No matter how disorganized things are, there's always one man who makes his way to the top. We must find out who that man is."

Cromwell consisted of two streets, one of them dead-ending on the other to form a T. Near the intersection of the T was a small wooden building with a tin roof and a sign that read SHERIFF. In small letters was the word JAIL. Tilghman parked his car beside the building and then stood in front of it for several minutes. He knew he was being observed and he gave them plenty of time to identify him.

When he entered the building he found a single room with bare studs and rafters. A rolltop desk was against one wall, a cot with greasy coverlet against the opposite one. In a corner was a coal stove and a single pan stained brown from boiled coffee. In the center of the room a pair of leg irons fastened by chain to a large piece of iron, a railroad car coupling.

Curious about his predecessor, Tilghman sat at the desk and examined the drawers. They contained some old WANTED posters that never got nailed up, a pack of worn cards which he saw at once were marked, an empty whiskey bottle, and an unopened bottle of home-brew beer with two inches of thick gray yeast settled in the bottom.

After a final look around his domain, Tilghman examined his gun (which he wore high on his hip and out of sight), then stepped outside to walk his beat, to let the rest of the town see him.

He walked slowly, studying the buildings, the alleyways. The structures had been thrown up without plan or paint. Most of them were single story, many with a high square façade meant to conceal the smallness of the room behind. If they were without grace or pride, there was an ugly lustiness about them, and they were sufficient to their job. There were dance halls, gambling parlors, bordellos, hotels, drug and hardware and clothing stores, a public bath.

As he walked the unpaved street Tilghman felt perfectly at home, for this oil boom town looked not unlike the land boom towns that had preceded it by half a century. There were some differences, certainly. In modern Cromwell there were no stacks of buffalo hides at the railroad siding, no vast cattle pens, and instead of horses at the hitching rails there were mud-caked Fords and Dodges. Also, Cromwell was surrounded by a strange and leafless forest—the wooden oil derricks. From them came the clank of cable tool drilling, and the pungency of new gushers.

The men who used this new town were not cowboys, dusty and thirsty from the trail, but old men—pipe liners, drillers, tool dressers, swampers and roustabouts—their clothes and hands and faces smeared black with the grease of their new trade.

And there was another important difference in the old towns and the new—crimes in the land boom days had been committed largely by amateurs, in Cromwell they were by professionals.

As Tilghman moved through town with deliberate step, several hundred men lined the streets to watch him, to measure him. Many made loud derisive comments. Midway down the first block he heard the kind of dialogue that was to follow him through this first day:

1st man: There's our new sheriff.
2nd man: Yeah? What's his name?
1st man: Tilghman. Bill Tilghman.
2nd man: You mean the man who was sheriff in Dodge City fifty years ago? Is he still alive?
1st man: (taking a hard look) I'd say, just barely. (Loud guffaws)

Tilghman ignored the taunts, his face was impassive. Whenever he was able to catch a man's eye he nodded his head. He made it a point to enter each building briefly in turn. It not only gave him a chance to learn the layout but also to judge the proprietor, marking him friend or foe.

He came to a drugstore, a skinny structure squeezed between two dance halls. When he entered he found the place empty except for the druggist who came forward to shake hands warmly.

"Sheriff, I'm right proud to shake your hand," he said. "The decent people of this town are countin' on you. This is a wicked town and I've always said that what we needed was a good sheriff and a good preacher. Well, we got the sheriff, and that's half the battle."

A customer entered the store and the druggist excused himself from Tilghman to wait on him. The disheveled and rheumy-eyed man walked to the back of the store with a strange, jerky gait and consulted with the druggist in low tones. The druggist handed him a small bottle of amber fluid and received one dollar for it. Observing the transaction, Tilghman guessed the bottle contained "Jake," a narcotic made of tincture of Jamaica ginger diluted with tricresol phosphate. It provided a cheap drunk but did great damage to a man's central nervous system. It attacked the spine, making it difficult for the victim to walk, finally paralyzing his legs.

When the customer left, Tilghman said to the druggist, "You're selling Jake?"

The druggist made an apologetic shrug.

"What do you charge for it?" asked Tilghman.

"One dollar for two ounces," the druggist said.

Tilghman rubbed his chin. "Costs you about eight cents to make and you sell it for a dollar. Pretty good profit."

"That's the going price," the druggist said, frowning. "I'm not charging any more than any other druggist."

"No, I reckon not."

"We're businessmen. We got a right to make a profit."

"You know what Jake does? Did you ever see a man who's been on Jake for a couple of years? He can't walk at all. His legs flop around as if he had nothing but empty trousers."

"I always tell 'em it's bad for 'em," the druggist said angrily. "I never sell a man Jake without warning him it's bad for him. But how come you're making such a fuss about this? It's not against the law to sell Jake."

"Well, I hope you hire that preacher soon. He might find a law to cover the situation for you."

Once outside the drugstore Tilghman regretted his words. He had made an enemy of a potential ally, and to no purpose. It was a serious tactical error and he felt a momentary pang—was this an indication that he was too old for the job?

The oil fields operated around the clock and as the six o'clock change drew near, Tilghman observed a number of strange rituals. A ladder was let down near him and a dozen men began to climb down from the flat roof of a hardware store.

"What's going on?" he asked of the first man down.

"There's no more space up there, Pop," the man said. "Go some place else."

Tilghman entered the store, introduced himself, and said, "Did you know there's a dozen men climbing down from your roof?"

The merchant nodded. "I rent 'em sleeping space."

"Sleeping space . . . on the roof?"

"Can you think of a safer place? When they're all up there they pull up the ladder, and don't let it down again until it's time to go to work. It may be a hard bed, but at least they ain't slugged and robbed in their sleep. Not many places in town as safe as my roof."

Tilghman couldn't help smiling. "And I thought I'd seen everything."

When he returned to the street he found the tempo of the town was speeding up; the raucous night sounds were setting in. Next to the hardware store was a public bath which consisted of water barrels hitched to rafters, the bottoms perforated to make a crude, unheated shower. The room was full of men just off the day shift, shouting and laughing and scrubbing, boasting about how much they would drink this night, how many girls they would have.

Music from the dance halls began to drift into the darkening streets. There was country music interspersed with such new jazz hits as *Yes! We Have No Bananas* and *Barney Google.* The dance hall next to the public bath was "Ma Murphy's." Tilghman entered it.

"Well, Marshal Tilghman, welcome, welcome." She was a big woman with brassy hair and a brassy voice, but a warm grin.

"You're Ma Murphy?" he asked, shaking hands.

"In the flesh," she guffawed, "all hundred and seventy pounds of me. You don't know me, Marshal, but I know you. When I was a kid my family homesteaded in the Cherokee Strip—you know, during the land runs in Oklahoma. A claim jumper moved in on us, but you came round and threw him off. You was a Federal man, and I never forgot you."

"Those were wild times," Tilghman smiled.

While they talked he observed the hall. It was made by rough carpentry, like all the other buildings in town, but boasted of one bit of decoration—on the wall behind the band there was painted a red setting sun. The band was composed of three slack-faced musicians playing piano, drum and saxophone. Along the sides of the room were benches where the "hostesses" sat between dances. At the front was a booth where the dance tickets were sold for ten cents each, and next to it a snack bar that offered hot dogs and coffee.

"In some ways this town is worse than anything back on the Strip," Ma Murphy was saying. "When I heard you was coming here I said to myself that if anybody can clean up Cromwell, it's Marshal Tilghman. But . . ."

"You don't think it can be done?"

"Let me tell you my setup," she said, avoiding a direct answer. "I run a strictly legitimate dance hall. Most of my hostesses are farm girls from around this area."

Tilghman looked at the hostesses and believed her. The

girls were plump and apple-cheeked, and they wore starched cotton dresses high at the throat.

"There are only two ways those girls go out of here," Ma Murphy said. "Either back to the farm or to the altar. And I don't sell no bootleg. I ain't saying that some of the boys don't bring it in on their hip, but I can't help that. And if any of them get out of line, I got a bouncer who throws them into the street. You just ask anybody in town about Ma Murphy and they'll tell you I run a straight place."

"I believe it," Tilghman said. "Tell me, Ma, do you pay protection?"

"And what if I do?" she said sharply. "You gonna arrest me?"

"No, I just want to know how this town runs . . . And who runs it."

"Well, I pay protection, all right! They're squeezin' me so hard I can hardly make a dime for myself."

"Who do you pay it to, Ma?"

She looked at him quizzically. "I ain't gonna tell you, Marshal. Not yet. I'll wait a couple of days until you've sized up the town. If I was to tell you now you wouldn't believe it."

It was 2 A.M. when Tilghman finally returned to his office to rest his feet and boil himself some coffee and think on what he had seen. There was fear in the town, certainly, and even spots of abject surrender; there was also hope, and some courage. But all these attitudes were in a state of suspension, in a sort of emotional deep freeze, and they would stay there until it came clear who would win the developing struggle. Without cynicism, Tilghman knew that his supporters would triple in number the moment he won the first battle. He tried not to think of the consequences if he lost it.

He was dozing in his chair when, at 3:15 A.M., three shots were fired in rapid succession. He came immediately awake and, old reflexes still working, rolled to his feet, gun in hand. By the time the third shot had been fired he had analyzed the situation. The gun was a good half-mile away, and therefore not aimed at him. From the hard, flat sound he knew it to be a pistol of fairly high caliber, probably a Colt .45. He returned his own gun to the holster, setting it loosely, and walked out the door and in the direction of the sound.

He did not run; to be winded unsteadied a man's aim. He turned a corner and saw, a half-block away, a young man standing in the middle of the street, holding his gun waveringly aloft and shouting his defiance into the night.

"Who's gonna take me?" he cried. "What sonofabitch thinks he's tough enough to take me?"

Tilghman had to make his judgment fast. Was this a trap? A provocation? If so, they probably did not plan to murder him, merely to test him, humiliate him, force him to panic and draw his own gun prematurely. On the other hand, if this boy was a loner and merely filled with whiskey courage, he wouldn't want to shoot, either. But having taken his position, made his statement, he would *have* to shoot if the sheriff pulled a gun.

The last thing Tilghman wanted to do was kill a man this first day on the job.

By now the kid saw Tilghman approaching and he leveled his gun, shouting, "You gonna take me? You think you can take me?"

"I'm the sheriff, son. Put your gun down."

"You gonna take me, Sheriff? Pull your gun."

Tilghman kept coming, his hands at his side.

"Pull your gun," the boy cried. "Goddam it, pull your gun!"

Tilghman was a yard away from the wavering barrel of the .45 when he stopped and held out his hand, palm up. "Give me your gun."

"Nobody's gonna take my gun, nobody!" He seemed close to tears.

"I'm not going to take it, you're going to give it to me."
Slowly the trembling hand came forward and surrendered
the gun. "You're an old man," the boy said bitterly. "I
couldn't shoot an unarmed old man."

"Of course you couldn't, son," Tilghman said, taking him
by the arm. "Now then, you want to go home or to jail?
It's one or the other."

"I'll go home," the boy said in a small voice.

Some thirty minutes later a half dozen men sat around
a kitchen table which held a quart of bootleg whiskey and
thick jelly glasses from which to drink it. These were city
men with soft hands, and they were discussing the events
of the evening. One of them said, with a reluctant admiration:

"The kid's gun was right in his belly and he didn't turn
a hair. He's sure got guts; I gotta say that."

There was gloomy agreement from all except one, a man
named Wiley Lynn. "The hell you say," he exclaimed in a
thin, strident voice. "It shows nothin' except that Tilghman's gone soft in the head. A young punk like that, liq-
uored up, hell, he could have pulled the trigger without
even knowin' what he was really doin', just be a reflex
action, a jumpy nerve." He poured himself a drink while
the rest pondered his words.

Wiley Lynn was something of a dandy. He dressed in
the fashion of the times, but with some exaggerations. The
shoulders of his suit contained extra padding, the double-
breasted lapels were cut a bit broader, the chalk stripes
in the brown fabric were just a little whiter. Though he was
only thirty-five, his thin face was lined from the excesses of
his life. He fancied himself a lady's man, and his habitual
expression was a leer.

"Hell, we're gonna have less trouble than I thought," he
said. "We'll have Tilghman run out of town by the end of
the week."

That Wiley Lynn misread Tilghman was not surprising;

he had had little experience with this kind of man. They came out of separate decades. Lynn was a Federal prohibition agent whose job was to enforce a law that few people wanted enforced. His official salary was only $2000 a year, but he made many times that in the graft he could exact because of his power to protect or prosecute.

The old-time lawmen of Tilghman's stamp had gone about their jobs quietly, conscious of the dignity of their office, proud of the respect accorded their badges. These things were alien to Wiley Lynn and when he saw the fatherly, almost gentle way in which Tilghman handled the young drunk, he could only conclude that age had softened him. Lynn could not know that Tilghman had arrested some of the most dangerous outlaws in the Old West without ever raising his voice. Perhaps his method of law enforcement was not suited to the new age, the new criminals, but Tilghman knew no other way.

2

Tilghman's parents, like most families coming to the Great Plains immediately after the Civil War, lived a life of trouble and danger. Such pioneers faced winter storms and parching summer heat, battled outlaws and Indians, raised their young or buried them, all in vast loneliness and with no resources but their own muscle, a gun and a plow. The struggle seemed worth it, for if they survived they would own part of the rich and precious land.

William Matthew Tilghman, Sr., did not fit the pattern, however. He lived on the frontier, partly because there was excitement, and partly because he just happened to be there. As a young man he served in the Army and was sent to Florida to "pacify" the Seminole Indians. This being accomplished in 1842, he was honorably discharged and obtained a contract to be a military sutler, selling provisions and liquor to the troops at Fort Dodge, Iowa. There he married Amanda Shepherd in 1846 and began to raise a family that finally consisted of three girls and three boys. William, Jr., was born on July 4, 1854.

The baby was but a month old when the father came home to announce, "They're gonna close the fort."

"You mean the Army is leaving?" Amanda asked.

"That's it."

"There is no more danger from Indians around here, then?"

"That's the way the Army sees it," he said.

A look of hope came on her face. "William, maybe now we can settle down, get some land."

"You mean become a farmer?" There was disbelief in his voice.

"This is good land," she said. "Lots of folks are homesteading."

He shook his head. "Amanda, you know I'm not cut out for that. I just couldn't stand all year in one place, looking at the ground for a seed to grow."

She sighed. "No, I reckon not. The land calls to some people, but not to you. What will we do, William?"

"Well, now, I haven't told you the good news, have I? I just had a talk with the colonel and he says he'll see my sutler contract is renewed if we go with him to the new base."

"Where would that be?"

"Fort Ridgley in Minnesota Territory."

"Sioux country," she said, more to herself than to her husband. "More fighting, more killing."

"I haven't told you the best part of it, Amanda. We're going up there by steamboat. Up the Mississippi and the Minnesota rivers by one of those elegant big boats with velvet curtains and crystal chandeliers and a big paddle wheel making a waterfall behind us. Won't that be grand?"

It was not so grand as William had anticipated. The elegant river boats—those with triple decks, with gaudy pictures on the paddle box, with card rooms and crystal chandeliers, writing rooms paneled with mahogany, with porcelain knobs on the doors and Wilton carpets in the staterooms—plied only between St. Louis and New Orleans. Those going north and west were small and graceless boats with two decks (one for cargo and one for passengers) and free of decoration.

The Tilghman family was installed on the upper deck, aft on the starboard side. They were the only civilians aboard,

the rest being soldiers on their way to Fort Ridgley. When
the boat was under way, William gestured toward the
decks full of guns, ammunition, blue-clad soldiers, and said,
"Nobody could be safer than us. One look at us is enough
to scare off those redskins. I bet we don't see an Indian the
whole trip."

He was right in his prediction they would not see an
Indian, but the Indians saw them. A thousand eyes lined
the banks of the upper Mississippi, and at night runners
and drums flashed the news ahead that the palefaces were
coming.

The boat had left the Mississippi and headed west on the
Minnesota River when the first arrow flew. It was mid-
morning of a peaceful, sun-warmed day, and the rhythmic
splash of the paddle wheel covered the slight hissing sound
of feathers in flight. But there came the solid sound of flint
being driven into wood, and a sergeant looked up to see the
arrow, still quivering, sticking out of an after bulkhead.

"Indians!" he bawled. "Indians, on the starboard!"

After some confusion there came a clatter of musketry
as the soldiers fired toward the enemy they could not see.
Gradually the firing ceased and the boat continued up-
stream with but the single arrow in its side. Just below
the arrow sat Amanda Tilghman, her face white as she
clutched the baby William against her. The arrow had
passed through the sleeve of her dress and grazed the baby's
head.

Her husband leaned anxiously over her. "You all right?"

She nodded but looked down at the child in her arms.
"It's an omen," she announced in a trembling voice. "He's
been born to a life of danger."

There was a conviction in America, held by soldier and
civilian alike, that the minute an Indian sees a blue army
uniform he will turn tail and run. There was scant basis for
this folk legend and certainly none was supplied at the new
Fort Ridgley. The Sioux had every intention of fighting for

their land, and the battle with the Army was still locked twenty-two years later when General Custer and his men were massacred in the Battle of the Little Bighorn.

After several years at Fort Ridgley, with no peace in sight, William gave in to his wife and agreed to go south to Kansas Territory which had been opened to homesteaders. They could not safely go by river, the Sioux controlled the banks, so they made the hazardous trip overland in a covered wagon. Good luck was with the family—they saw not a single Indian.

The Tilghman homestead was located four miles southwest of Atchison, Kansas, near the Missouri River. Amanda thought that her family was in a place of safety and peace, but she was wrong. There were midnight raids, burnings and shootings, the only difference from the past being that neither raider nor victim was a redskin—all were white. This was "Bleeding Kansas" where the pro-slavery men and the free-soil men were battling to control the territory.

In 1855 the free-soil men met to adopt an anti-slavery constitution and asked to be admitted to the Union. Kansas was admitted on January 29, 1861, and Amanda Tilghman, along with thousands of other wives and mothers in the new state, sighed with relief that peace was come at last. Two and a half months later Fort Sumter was fired upon and the Civil War began.

Five weeks later Tilghman came home from a visit to Atchison and said, "Amanda, I've got to go to war."

There was neither anger nor tears from Amanda, she had known he would go. The whole family traveled to Atchison the following day for the swearing-in ceremony. William Tilghman looked smart in his new blue uniform with sergeant's stripes on the sleeve, but Amanda's eyes were upon the young drummer boy—her firstborn, Richard. When father and son marched away together, she climbed slowly back into the wagon, suddenly enfeebled. Young Bill climbed up beside her and took the reins in his hands. He was going on seven.

3

The family went on as before, caught in a routine they could not alter. Their lives were tied to the sun and the seasons; there was a time to plant and a time to harvest, and a time to repeat the cycle. All the children worked in the fields, but as the eldest, William, Jr., had extra duties and privileges. He took down his father's muzzle-loading gun to hunt for game. Though the gun was almost as tall as he was, he managed to aim it with the aid of a rest stick and kept the family supplied with quail, rabbit and duck.

Few strangers came by the Tilghman land and when one did it was cause for excitement. Bill was twelve, driving the team and wagon home from a blackberry hunt, when he saw a plume of dust on the horizon, which meant a horse and rider were coming his way. Within minutes the rider pulled up beside the wagon and doffed his hat to Bill and to his sisters.

"Good afternoon, sir, and ladies."

The girls giggled and covered their mouths with their hands. "Good afternoon," Bill replied, blushing for the silliness of his sisters.

"I'm looking for a man driving a team of mules and a covered wagon. Did you happen to see anything like that?"

Bill didn't answer at once, he was so lost in admiration he

hardly heard the question. Never had he seen a man so
dashing as this stranger who wore his hair shoulder length
beneath a broad plainsman's hat. His shirt was of softest
deerskin, his jacket of brown buckskin with leather fringes
across the back and down the sleeves. At his waist hung a
pair of gleaming pistols.

Even more impressive than his clothing was his grand
manner, his unhurried gallantry. Surely there was nothing
such a man couldn't do!

"Son, I asked if you'd seen a pair of mules and a wagon."
There was a slight stiffening in the voice.

"Oh, yes, sir," Bill answered quickly. "We did see them,
back that way a couple of miles. They were headed toward
Atchison."

The man looked down the road, his eyes squinting against
the low sun. "This road leads straight to Atchison?"

"Yes, sir."

"I thank you, and good day." He swept his hat off in a
salute of farewell, spurred his horse and galloped away.

Later that week Bill drove to town for supplies and bought
a copy of the local newspaper. The lead story read:

> Atchison had a distinguished visitor this week. Mr. . . .
> Hickok, famous marshal of Abilene, known as "Wild
> Bill"; the most expert pistol shot in the West. He is now
> a deputy U. S. Marshal and scout at Fort Hays, and
> came here, following for four hundred miles a stolen
> team of mules and wagon. The thief had just sold them,
> but Wild Bill nabbed him before he left town, and took
> back the stolen property.

One evening several months later Bill said, "Ma, I'm going
to be a scout and a lawman." Impulsively she grabbed
her son and held him hard against her. "Not right away,
Ma. I won't leave until Pa gets back from the war."

The war ended at Appomattox on April 9, 1865, and William Tilghman and his drummer son, Richard, came home. The father was blinded in one eye but was otherwise sound and, having quenched his thirst for adventure, became a surprisingly able farmer. He moved his family into a larger house, installed a Negro tenant farmer in the old one. Frontier violence and danger had moved on west and the Tilghman family settled in to long, sunny seasons of peace and even affluence.

Young Bill had said no more about being a scout and his mother hoped he had forgotten the idea. He hadn't.

"Met a couple of fellows in town," he announced at the supper table one evening. "They're going west to hunt buffalo."

"Dangerous," his father said laconically.

"Good money in it," he countered. "I hear they're paying five dollars a hide. Besides, it's not dangerous if you know how."

"*You* know how?"

"I can learn," Bill said stoutly.

After a moment of silence the father said, with a sigh, "Yes, I reckon you can . . . if you're dead set."

Amanda sat quite still and stared vacantly at the table before her. Finally she spoke in a small, dry voice. "When would you be going, Billy?"

"Tomorrow, Ma."

William Tilghman rode with his son to Atchison the following day and met the partners in the project. Their names were Jude Bucknum and Oliver Rife, and they were only slightly older than Bill. William discovered that they too were greenhorns, but they shared with his son what was, perhaps, the essence of youth—a sublime self-confidence. The father observed it with sadness and envy.

The boys' equipment consisted of a team of horses and a flatbed wagon, tent and blankets, guns and ammunition. Young Bill's weapons were a pair of cap and ball pistols. He had practiced with them until he could kill a prairie chicken or a rabbit at forty yards—shooting with either hand. Yet a pistol, however deadly against a chicken or a rabbit, was no match for a charging buffalo.

William reached into the back of the wagon and removed something hidden beneath a blanket. He handed it to his son, saying, "Billy, I want you to have this."

The boy stared, open-mouthed, at what he knew was his father's prize possession—a Sharps rifle. It had a long range with high accuracy and took .40 caliber ammunition for maximum penetration. It had been designed and manufactured with jeweler precision by inventor and master gunsmith Christian Sharps. These guns had been highly favored by the U. S. Cavalry during the Civil War and, as a result, had acquired an aura of invincibility. When William Tilghman came home from the war he hung his Sharps above the fireplace and no one had been allowed to handle it—until this moment.

Even now young Bill was reluctant to touch the gun. "Pa . . . you're sure . . . ?"

"I'm sure, Billy."

The boy took the gun and fondled it for a moment, then impulsively embraced his father. It was the only time in their lives they were able to make such a gesture of love and gratitude.

4

Young Bill climbed to the wagon seat and took the reins, thus assuming leadership of the expedition. He had the proper credentials; he owned the best gun, was the best shot, and had been west before. When sixteen he had gone to the plains and the mountains beyond on a small-game hunting trip with two cousins, and so he knew what lay ahead.

He cracked the whip expertly above the horses' heads, and they leaned hard against the harness collars. The wagon groaned, then moved.

"We'll follow the Santa Fe Trail 'til we come to the Great Bend of the Arkansas River," he said. "Then we can ask which is the best way to go."

"Why don't we just bust on straight west until we come to a buffalo herd and begin shooting?" Oliver Rife demanded. "That's what we come out here for."

Bill gave him a scornful look. "It's easy enough to shoot them, Ol, but that's only half the job. The other half is selling them. After we kill them, we gotta skin them, cut out the steaks and the roasts, pile the hides and the meat on the wagon, and then get it to a market and sell it before it goes bad. We gotta hunt near a railroad town where the hides can be shipped east."

"How about Dodge City, Bill?" Jude Bucknum asked.

Bill nodded judiciously. "A lot of hides are shipped east out of Dodge on the Santa Fe line. And up northwest there is Hays on the Kansas Pacific Railroad. We can decide between them when we get to the Arkansas River."

Two weeks later the creaking wagon and the young hunters came out upon an elevation called Pawnee Rock. At their feet was the valley of the Arkansas River sweeping northward in its great bend, its shores fringed with cottonwood, willow and elm. Beyond were the great plains, short grass country across which had rolled the prairie schooners of the pioneers headed for California, the pack mules of prospectors determined to dig gold from the Rockies, the hell-for-leather couriers of the Pony Express. It was a land of blistering heat in the summer and bitter winds in the winter. It was the home of the buffalo. After staring, awestruck, the boys turned toward the town of Hays.

Arriving at Hays, Kansas, the boys found a village of a half-dozen houses, a barracks-like hotel, a saloon and restaurant, a livery stable and a railway depot, all devoted to the town's one industry—buffalo. It was from this base that the hunters went out into the plains, and here they returned with their kill. A wooden platform beside the depot was piled with hides tied with sinews in bundles of ten, waiting shipment back east. In the building's meager shade was the meat, purplish red and glutinous, wearing a halo of flies. When the wind was right the traveler could smell Hays long before sighting it.

The liveryman, his chair tilted against the stable wall and his hat pulled over his eyes, dozed. Having the only stable in town, he found no need to stir himself. He heard the team and wagon pull up and three pairs of boots jump to the ground, but he didn't deign to open his eyes.

"We'd like to rent some horses, sir," Bill Tilghman said.

The liveryman didn't move for a long moment, then with a gesture of weary patience, he shoved back his hat and opened his eyes. He studied the three young men and then spat derisively into the dust at his feet.

"We'd like to rent some horses," Bill repeated.

"What fer?"

"Hunting!"

"Oh, you must mean for rabbits."

"I mean for buffalo," Bill said firmly.

"Good God Almighty!" the man moaned, looking heavenward. "Everybody thinks he can be a buffalo hunter. Bookkeepers and ribbon clerks comin' out here thinkin' they're hunters."

Jude spoke up angrily. "We ain't bookkeepers nor ribbon clerks."

"You ain't dry behind the ears, neither," the liveryman said.

Bill held out a hand to silence Jude. To the man he said, "We got the money to rent." He pulled a roll of bills from his pocket.

"You ever hunt buffalo?" the liveryman demanded, but the sight of money had taken the sting out of his words.

"No," Bill answered reluctantly.

"You'll probably get my horses kilt, and yourselves, too." But he stood up and led the three boys into the stable.

After the horses had been selected, saddled, and hitched to the back of the wagon, the liveryman said to Bill, "You know where you shoot a buffalo to kill him?"

"His heart. Just behind the front shoulder and halfway up his chest."

"Iffen you don't get a clear shot at the heart it's better not to shoot at all. Buffalo is peaceful enough critters until they're wounded or scared, then look out! Ever seen a stampede? It's something a man ain't ever likely to forget. They pack together when they start to move, a couple thousand of 'em, and they run wild-eyed, shoulder to shoulder. You can feel the ground shake when they're miles away. Yer pony can't outrun 'em, yer only chance is to outflank 'em, get outta their path. Iffen you don't, yer done. Their hooves cut up everything. I seen a railway car once that had been on a siding when a stampede come across. Nothin' left but sawdust. The iron wheels had been driven right into the ground."

The boys were impatient to be off, but they listened to his story with sober faces. Their hunting trip suddenly seemed less of a lark. "Thanks for the advice," Bill said, mounting his horse.

"And another thing," the man called. "Don't make camp too far from the trail. Indians, ya know."

"Yeah, I know."

"You ever see a scalped man? Why, not more 'n a month ago . . ."

He didn't get a chance to finish his story, for the young hunters were under way, heading west.

For some time the boys rode in silence, each speculating on the Indian story the liveryman had started to tell. It would have been better, perhaps, if they had heard it out, for the facts could not have been more gory than scenes of their imaginations. From time to time each boy surreptitiously looked at the horizons, but there was neither buffalo nor Indians—the short, fragrant grass ran to the sky in all directions. The very emptiness of the landscape seemed threatening and they spoke little.

The sun had begun to drop in the west when Bill said, "Let's make camp."

They unsaddled their horses, took the team out of the traces, fed and watered them and tethered them to the wagon for the night. At last it was time to feed themselves.

"Do we build a fire?" Jude asked.

They looked at each other and discovered that none knew the answer to the simple question.

"The smoke might scare off any buffalo hereabouts," Oliver said.

Jude spoke their real concern: "It might attract Indians."

"I dunno," Bill said, "but I guess we better not."

They ate their supper cold, cleaned their tin plates by

scrubbing them with dirt and grass, pitched the small tent and crawled into it to lie close together. They were too excited to fall asleep immediately and for a time they boasted about what they would do tomorrow, how many buffalo they would kill. At last the talk ran down and there was silence and blackness and the fragrance of the grass crushed beneath their bodies and they slipped into sleep.

No one knew how long they had been asleep, maybe an hour or two, but suddenly they were rigidly awake. It came again, the noise that had wakened them, and it was an animal howl. It was not a howl of pain, but seemingly one of sorrow. It started with a bark and then rose wavering a full octave, held the high, clear note for about five seconds, then fell away to end in a sigh.

Bill expelled his held breath and said, "Nothin' but a coyote."

"Yeah," the others agreed.

"I hear they follow a buffalo herd," Jude said. "They wait for the old ones or the sick ones to fall out, then they get a meal."

"Then there must be a herd nearby," Bill said.

There was a long and thoughtful silence which was finally broken by Oliver. "I never heard of a stampede at night."

"No," Bill said firmly. "I never heard of one, either."

But sleep did not return easily.

They were up at dawn, packed, saddled and on the move within the hour. They rode slowly, every nerve alert. At mid-morning the horses became nervous, dancing at the slightest noise, the most innocent shadow.

"The horses smell them," Bill said, "so we must be down wind of the herd. That's lucky."

Fifteen minutes later they, too, heard the sound and reined their horses. "Thunder?" Oliver asked. They listened, and it was not thunder. The sound was a low monotone, a sort of grumbling.

"Look there!" Bill cried, pointing south.

There was a herd of buffalo, thousands of the animals, so

many they seemed to fill the horizon. They were grazing and the sound was a throaty grunting each animal made as it savored the sweet grass.

Bill pulled his Sharps rifle from the saddle holster. Since he was the best shot it had been agreed that he would lead the approach and make the first kill. They advanced upon the herd at a slow trot. At a hundred yards away they were completely ignored by the animals; at fifty yards a few of them raised their massive heads in mild curiosity but returned almost at once to grazing. At twenty yards Bill reined his horse, sighted his rifle and fired. It was a perfect hit and a buffalo fell on its side, kicked twice, then was still.

Two more shots rang out, but neither Jude nor Oliver had made a clean kill and two wounded bulls bellowed and plunged. Would this frighten the herd, cause a stampede? Alarmed, all three boys pumped bullets into the wounded animals and finally brought them to the ground. Winded from the excitement, they pulled their ponies off a bit while they reloaded and observed the effect on the herd. It was one of dumb surprise. Those nearest the dead stood about with spread legs, their small eyes red and staring, their nostrils quivering at the odor of blood. They began to back away, lowing as they went, but could not go far because of the grazing animals behind them.

Having reloaded, the boys spurred their ponies forward again, shooting as they came. Another buffalo went down, and another. Alarm began to spread deeper into the herd, causing little eddies, then whirlpools of motion in the great sea of beasts. Fear became contagious and the herd began to run—the outer edge of it first, moving counterclockwise around the massive center, at last turning it, sweeping it into terror and headlong flight.

The animals were ranked so closely that their plunging shoulders, glossy in the sunlight, looked like waves in a storm —a mighty river cascading over the plain.

The hunters rode beside the herd, firing and reloading and firing, until their arms were weary and their horses exhausted. At last they pulled up and watched the herd thunder on toward the horizon. The trembling ground beneath their feet gradually stilled. When they looked backward they saw the path they had come; it was marked by the strewn bodies of dead buffalo.

"Yowee!" Jude exulted. "Lookee that! Must be a hundred of them. We're real ram-damn buffalo hunters."

"We're rich!" Oliver cried. "There's at least three hundred dollars lyin' there. Mebbe more. Ain't that so, Bill?"

"Not lyin' *there*," Bill corrected, "but waiting back in Hays when we deliver the hides and the meat. So let's get to work skinning them."

"Aw, come on," Jude objected. "That was a hard ride and I'm tuckered. Let's rest awhile."

Bill looked up at the sky. "About midday, which means we got about six hours of sun left. We gotta get those hides off and staked out on the ground to sun-dry."

"I'm gonna rest a bit," Jude said sulkily.

"Do as you like," Bill said, "but if you don't do a third of the work you're sure not gonna get a third of the money. And besides, if we don't get these animals skinned right away, the Indians may come and do it for us."

That was a potent argument and Jude gave a quick, apprehensive look around the horizon. The three of them dismounted and went to work.

What followed for the next few days was pure drudgery. Not only did the hides of the enormously heavy animals have to be stripped, scraped and staked out to dry, but then the carcasses had to be cut up with no tool but a simple hunting knife. Hides and meat were at last piled on the wagon and hauled back to Hays, trip after trip. It was a desperate race against time—the time Indians might appear, the time the meat would spoil.

When the last hide and carcass had been delivered and paid for and the money divided three ways, Bill said, "I'm gonna buy the horse I been riding. He's a good buffalo pony and there's no sense paying rent on him all the time."

"Not me," Jude said. "I'm using my money for a *big* party."

"Where you goin'?" Oliver asked.

"I don't rightly know. I'm just headin' back east until I come to the first saloon with dancin' girls . . . and that's the place. I'm gonna give those girls a treat, lettin' them know a real ram-damn buffalo hunter."

"Yeah," Oliver grinned. "How about you, Bill?"

"No, I gotta buy this horse and . . ."

"Damn it, Bill," Jude exploded, "this is the hardest money I ever earned and I intend to get some pleasure out of it."

"So do I," Bill said, looking out at the great plain. There was a fresh breeze running across the pale, sweet grass, rippling it into silver waves. Feathery clouds moved at stately pace across the arch of blue, sailing toward that distant, mysterious, never found spot where sky and land meet.

Bill said softly, "I like it out there."

5

Jude and Oliver never returned to the plains; Bill Tilghman remained to become one of the most skilled and resourceful buffalo hunters in the West. The demand for meat and hide was so great that he eventually hired his own crew of specialists. He did the hunting, and the trail of carcasses he left was followed by skinners, butchers and draymen. No village or military post ran short of food if it contracted Tilghman for the job.

When the Atchison, Topeka & Santa Fe Railroad laid tracks to Fort Dodge, a new town began to grow there (Dodge City) and eighteen-year-old Tilghman won the contract to supply meat. From September 1, 1871, to April 1, 1872, Bill killed and delivered 3000 buffalo. This became an all-time record, surpassing the previous one made by his childhood hero, Wild Bill Hickok.

Unlike many hunters, Bill received no pleasure from the killing. It was a job to be done, one which allowed him to live out-of-doors. His great adventure was pitting himself against the plains, surviving their moods. Strong winds blew over them for months at a time, there were no trees to offer shade and fuel, and little surface water to drink.

The storms came in infinite variety and were like nothing Bill had ever experienced. Riding alone one afternoon, soon after Jude and Oliver had left, the sky suddenly darkened. One moment the sun was shining and the next moment it was blotted out by a mass of angry clouds. The air filled with the smell of sulphur and the horse reared and whinnied in terror. A lurid purple light began to play against the black horizon and there was a series of deafening explosions—it sounded as if the world were cracking open to reveal the pits of hell. Up from those pits came golden balls of fire that cannonaded over the surface of the prairie with some deadly purpose.

As quickly as the electrical storm had come, it disappeared, leaving the plains sunny and serene, leaving the young hunter shaken and wondering if it had really happened.

Spectacular and dangerous were the prairie fires that were occasionally ignited by the lightning. A wall of flame advancing with the speed of the wind that drove it could seldom be outrun. Tilghman learned how to survive by starting his own counterfire. As soon as he had burned off the dry grass in a large circle he'd stand in the middle of it, safe from the advancing flames that could only sweep around him.

In springtime there was the danger of flash floods. A heavy downpour could change an innocent looking dry gulch into a raging torrent that could batter and drown any living thing in its path. In the dry fall season there were dust storms so dense as to hide the sun. There was no escaping from the grit, it seeped into ears and nose and eyes, temporarily blinding men and animals. And when it passed, the landscape was altered, drifts had covered the trail.

The winter storms were the most savage. Men were caught and pinned down by the swirling whiteness that made all directions the same, pressed upon by subzero temperatures that slowly ate into the very marrow of their bones. They sometimes slaughtered their own horses, ripped them open to crawl into the hot, bloody cavity.

These forces of nature shaped young Bill Tilghman. At

eighteen his slender body was all sinew. On his square, weathered face there was a jutting nose and gray eyes that seemed distant, as if forever focused on the horizon. He was laconic; like many men who lead solitary lives he had discovered how superfluous was most conversation. He was friendly but with a becoming shyness, his word was totally trusted by everyone who knew him.

One of the reasons he was so successful as a buffalo hunter was that he had less trouble with the Indians than most white hunters. Contrary to common practice, he did not invade the Indian hunting grounds, and the chiefs knew this. And too, he admired the Indians, enjoyed their company and found them handsome. The Plains Indians—Kansa, Pawnee, Sioux, Cheyenne, Blackfeet, Crow and Arapaho—had a striking resemblance to each other. Their foreheads receded above an angular face with a large aquiline nose, high cheekbones, full mouth and jutting chin. They decorated themselves imaginatively with paint and feathers, and moved with grace.

They were not agricultural people, but hunters, and they depended upon buffalo for all their needs. There was fresh meat for the summertime, then it was dried and pounded into pemmican for winter food; the skin provided clothing, as well as shields and tepees; the animal sinews made thread and bow strings; the bone was shaped into arrowheads. Without buffalo the tribes faced hunger, cold and death.

The white man thought the buffalo herds were limitless but the Indian knew better; he knew that each time an animal was slaughtered and carted east, his tribe was diminished. In the end there was no alternative but war. Bill Tilghman saw it coming but was powerless to avoid it. No matter how scrupulous he might be about the Indian hunting grounds he was caught up in the larger conflict. To be a buffalo hunter was to be, inevitably, an Indian fighter.

The seven tribes of Plains Indians had no common spoken language but had developed a complicated sign language for communication. For decades they had warred on each other, but with the coming of the white man they made more or less common cause in defense of their hunting lands. They were among the finest physical specimens of the race; tall and deep chested, they moved with grace and hauteur. They were, perhaps, the finest horsemen in the world, and after they obtained rifles they became excellent marksmen, formidable foes.

In the spring of 1872 the streets of Dodge City were being staked out and the first buildings under construction when a significant event took place—though it seemed commonplace enough at the time.

Shortly after dawn Bill was shaken awake by George Rust, an occasional partner in buffalo hunts. In fact, they had planned to ride out together on this day.

"Bill, wake up . . . wake up," George said. "Come outside and have a look."

Pulling on his leather pants, Bill stepped outside the railroad bunkhouse and looked in the direction George was pointing. Low on the western horizon was a haze of white smoke.

"Prairie fire," Bill said.

"It's a damn sure big one."

Bill nodded in agreement. "You know the best thing to do with a prairie fire? Stay away from it. We won't be hunting today."

For three days the smoke marched the horizon, moving in a southerly direction. On the fourth day the air was clear and Bill and George Rust saddled up and rode out. They were gone the rest of the week and when they returned their faces were grim. Bill went directly to the railroad superintendent with whom he had the meat contract.

"I got bad news," he said. "There's no buffalo on the entire northern section of the range."

The superintendent looked at him, disbelieving. "How's that possible?"

"The Indians, Cheyenne mostly, moved into the range in small groups and fired it. They burned from a hundred miles north and west of Walnut Creek to the Colorado Territory, the whole north range. They drove the herds south across the Arkansas River."

The superintendent said, "Well, all you gotta do is hunt south of the river instead of north."

"But that's Indian Territory."

"Hell's fire, what difference does that make? I got a contract with you to supply my men with meat. There ain't nothin' in that contract that says where you're to get the meat, it just says that you damn well better get it."

Bill frowned and studied his boots. The older man looked at him closely. "Are you scared, son? Tell me the truth, 'cause if you are you're no more good to me and I'll hire some men who ain't."

"I'm not scared," Bill said, "it's just . . . well, the Indians have to live, too. I don't know that hunting in Indian Territory is right."

The railroad man struck his own forehead with the palm of his hand and cried, "Right?! Right?! God Almighty! We're trying to make something of this country, trying to civilize it, and when a band of bloodthirsty savages invade our grazing land . . . *our* land by *agreement* . . . you suddenly don't know what's the right thing to do!" He gestured toward the south. "Them's our buffalo down there, they come from our land, they been stolen from us. All I'm expecting you to do is to hunt buffalo that belonged to us in the first place. Now, you got any confusion as to the rightness of that?"

Bill rubbed his chin. "I guess I never thought about it that way."

"Well, you better start thinking about it that way . . . and real quick."

The following day Bill saddled up, packed his supplies and headed south into Indian country. He went alone because he wanted to be inconspicuous and he wanted to travel fast. On the morning of the second day he came upon a great herd grazing and grunting. He made camp a mile off and then began to approach the herd. The wind was unfavorable for an open approach so he flanked the herd, then dismounted and began to belly-up—lying flat on the ground and hitching himself forward on knees and elbows. He carried his Sharps rifle, a rest stick on which he could support the rifle for distant shots; a newly purchased Colt .45 hung from his belt on the right side, and on the left a pouch containing additional ammunition for both Sharps and Colt. In his belt was stuck the skinning knife.

If he had not been so intent on the buffalo he might have reacted sooner to the rattle. Instead, he was completely unaware of the danger until the rattlesnake raised its flat head above the grass eighteen inches away. The malevolent little eyes measured the distance to Bill's face, then the snake struck. Bill jerked his head to one side and the fangs hissed past his ear. The snake's body was draped full length over his shoulder and along his back. He rolled to the right, shaking free of the snake, and came to his knees with the Colt in his hand. A single shot and the snake's headless body writhed on the ground. Breathing heavily, Bill returned the Colt to the holster and stared down at the nearness of death.

There came to his ears a strange rippling sound. It came from behind him and he slowly turned around to find himself facing five Cheyenne on horseback, rifles cradled in their arms. He considered the odds against him—five to one. His Sharps rifle lay on the ground out of reach, which left him with the Colt and five bullets. Could he kill five Indians with five quick shots? It was barely possible, but only if he got the jump on them, if he shot first. And he knew he could not bring himself to do that, he could not kill except in self-defense.

He stood quite still, his feet spread to balance his weight on his toes, his right hand hung with curved fingers inches from the butt of his Colt.

The rippling sound came again and it was laughter, friendly laughter. The Indians pointed to the headless snake in admiration of his kill. "*Poweh, poweh*," they said, which meant "good." Then they crossed their breasts, the gesture of peace. Bill crossed his in return, and let out his breath.

"Chuckaway," one of the Indians said, rubbing his belly. They were hungry and asking for food. Bill had some fairly fresh buffalo meat in his saddlebag, so he pointed toward his camp and motioned the Indians to follow him. One of the Indians jerked out a hair from his pony's tail, tied a loop of it around the snake and dragged it behind him to Bill's camp. It was, after all, food.

Bill served up a banquet of buffalo meat, bread, molasses and coffee. There was much appreciative smacking of lips among the Indians, and when the meal was complete and it was time to leave, they indicated the white hunter was welcome to come to their camp for a return meal. Bill promised that one day he would do so. The Indians again crossed themselves in peace and rode away.

When Bill returned to Dodge he went to the railroad superintendent and said, "There are great herds between the Arkansas River and the Cimarron. I can keep you supplied with meat."

6

That fall there was an exchange of letters between Bill and his oldest brother Dick who had remained on the family farm back in Kansas. Dick wrote:

Mom and Dad are fine. Mary, Josephine, Harriet and Frank are good, too, and send their best. Crops have been pretty good. Soon as we get the harvest in I'd like to come out and hunt some buffalo with you. How about it? Faithfully, your brother, Richard.

Bill wrote back: *Come ahead. Meet me in Dodge. My love to everybody, Bill.*

When the brothers met in Dodge they grinned and pounded each other on the back. It had been only two years since they had seen each other, but they were both conscious of change. Dick was weathered and strong, but with the thick, solid body of a man who works the land. He had none of the lean, flat muscles that marked Bill, none of the rawhide stamina that comes with living in a saddle.

There was another change. Dick had always enjoyed the authority of the oldest son, and the added prestige of having been a drummer boy in the Civil War. Now the roles were reversed; it was the younger brother who was in charge. Part of the reason was, of course, that Bill was the experienced hunter, Dick the inexperienced one. But more than that,

Dick saw in his younger brother a new self-possession, even a quiet dignity, the kind that comes to a man who has been tested. If Dick felt a twinge of envy, it was quickly smothered by a family pride.

"First thing is to get you outfitted with a good horse and a good buffalo gun," Bill said.

"You still got Pa's old Sharps rifle?" Dick asked.

"I sure have. Best buffalo gun ever made. It was originally a .40 caliber, you remember? Well, I shot the barrel smooth, completely wore out the rifling, and I sent it back to the factory and they rebored it to a .45-.60. I wouldn't take a good deal for that gun."

"Pa will be pleased to hear that."

Bill explained their hunting plans. "Buffalo's farther away than they used to be, some big herds even south of the Cimarron, which means we gotta take enough supplies to set up a series of dugout camps a couple days' ride apart."

"How soon we get going?" Dick asked eagerly.

"Just as soon as we get outfitted. Say, tomorrow morning. That be soon enough for you?"

"That'd be just fine."

The brothers left Dodge the following morning and made their first camp at Horseshoe Bend on Elm Creek. They found game at once and Dick got his first buffalo. They were in the process of skinning it when Dick glanced toward the west and his face went white.

"Indians!" he said hoarsely. "My God, Indians on the warpath!"

"You don't know they're on the warpath," Bill said. "Be calm. Be friendly."

There were twenty Cheyenne in the party, all mounted on good ponies. The Plains Indians had domesticated the wild mustang, offspring of horses left behind by the Spanish two centuries before. The Cheyenne reined up in front of the camp and dismounted, the chief stepping forward. Bill walked toward him, made the Indian cross of peace and then extended his hand. The chief shook it, then removed a

folded sheet of paper from a leather pouch and gave it to
Bill. It read:

The bearer, Little Robe, chief of the Cheyenne, is a good
Indian. He has been to Washington and is a friend of the
government. He has authority to arrest any white hunters
found trespassing in the Indian Territory, and to deliver
them to the commanding officer at Fort Supply.

Bill had just finished reading the letter when Dick
shouted, "Hey, they're stealing our stuff!"

Several of the Indians had moved in behind Bill and were
taking what equipment struck their fancy. One of them
had gathered up the skinning knives.

"Drop those knives!" Bill ordered, stepping close to the
red man. Bill doubled his fist, cocked it for a blow, and
repeated his demand, "Drop those knives."

For a long moment the Indian looked at him impassively,
but then slowly opened his arms and the knives fell to the
ground. The Indian stepped back a few paces and made the
sign of peace. From the corner of his eye Bill saw that another Indian had picked up a rifle, it was his cherished
Sharps.

"Take that rifle away from him!" he shouted to his
brother. Dick jumped forward, grabbed the rifle by the
barrel, the Indian held onto the stock, and they struggled
back and forth. Drawing his Colt, Bill aimed it directly at
the Indian's head and walked slowly toward him. The Indian
let go of the gun, stepped back and made the sign of peace.

Throughout the brief skirmish Chief Little Robe stood
apart, observing. Bill now returned the letter and said,
"Washington admired Chief Little Robe and knows he is not
a thief. Washington would be sad to learn that some of the
great chief's braves are thieves. I will not tell Washington
because I know the great chief will not let his braves steal
again."

The chief took back his Washington letter, folded it, put
it in the leather pouch that hung from his waist, gave the
sign of peace, and mounted his horse. He spoke a single,

guttural order and his braves mounted their horses and they all rode off without a backward look.

"*Whew-w-w*," Dick breathed. "I don't mind admitting I was scared."

"Yeah," Bill grinned. "So was I."

"You sure didn't look it," his brother said admiringly. "When you pulled your pistol on that Indian you sure looked like you was gonna drill him right between the eyes."

"That's what I wanted him to think."

"Bill, would you have shot him or was it bluff?"

"I don't really know. I was pretty sure they'd back off. I was doing what they expected me to do."

"Expected?"

"Let me tell you something I've figured out about Indians, at least the Plains tribes. They're strong and they're brave and they're smart, but they're kinda like children, too. They get away with as much as they can, but if they're caught doin' something wrong they expect to be punished. Just now they knew they were wrong in trying to steal, and they knew I was right in refusing to let them. There's no hard feelings about it, and the next time we see Chief Little Robe he'll be friendly as anything."

"And he won't pull that Washington letter any more?"

"Maybe on other white hunters, but not likely on us. He lost some face just now and he won't want to be reminded. As far as he and I are concerned, this meeting never happened."

"I'll be damned," Dick said. "Shooting buffalo is more complicated than I thought."

Bill's prediction was right; the next time he met Little Robe they ate together without either mentioning the attempted thefts. Bill was frequent host to other Cheyenne notables—Little Bear, the war chief, and Roman Nose, a redoubtable warrior. He was on intimate terms with Kicking Bird and White Deer of the Kiowas, and from time to time entertained the chief of the Arapaho. For a white man, he was held in high respect. He could outride most of the In-

dians, had outshot all of them. Most important, he did not
boast about his prowess, did not use them to humiliate the
red men.

Despite the mutual respect and even affection between
Bill Tilghman and the Indians, they were destined to become enemies. As the buffalo herds diminished, the last of
the great Indian wars became inevitable. There was no formal declaration of war, no fixed battle lines, each tribe went
separately on the warpath when pressed too hard by the
white hunters or the white settlers.

In the spring of 1874 Bill and his brother stopped in at
the camp of White Deer and received food and hospitality,
as was the custom. After riding on a few miles, Bill turned in
his saddle to look at Dick and said, "Did you notice anything unusual at White Deer's camp?"

"No. I don't think I did."

"White Deer wasn't there."

"They said he was off hunting."

"All the rest of the tribe's hunters were there. And White
Deer doesn't hunt alone. I think he was there all the time
but refused to see us. And last week when we stopped at
Little Robe's camp he was absent, too."

"That's right!"

"They said he was in council. But all of his braves were
with us. Who was he sitting in council with?"

"Golly. What do you make of it?"

"I think they're telling us that we're not welcome in
their camps any more."

"You mean they're getting ready to go on the warpath?"

"I don't know. Might be. Or it might be I've offended
them somehow. I just don't know."

"How in hell could *you* have offended them? You treat
them like they was white men. What could they be mad
at you about?"

Bill rode in troubled silence for a minute. Then he said,
"I'm killing buffalo."

"There's enough for everybody."

"Maybe . . ."

"If you don't supply Dodge, someone else will."

"Oh, I've got a contract with Dodge and I'll carry it out. But I wish I knew what was going on in those Indians' minds."

All that day they trailed a herd that had headed west, but in midafternoon Bill cut away from the trail and turned south.

"Kicking Bird has his camp about an hour's ride south," he said to Dick. "I think we'll make a call on him."

"Might be dangerous."

"Might be," Bill admitted, "but I want to know what's going on. I can talk to Kicking Bird, or I always have been able to in the past. Worth a try."

The sun was low when the two white men rode into Kicking Bird's camp of thirty tepees. They had been here before and their presence did not cause any commotion except among the children who ran beside them. They pulled up in front of the largest tepee where Kicking Bird's two wives were busy tanning a buffalo hide. Bill asked for the chief and one of the wives responded in sign language.

"What'd she say?" Dick asked in a low voice.

"She says Kicking Bird is in council."

"Same old run-around. Let's get out of here."

"No, let's stay and see what we can find out."

"Bill, I don't like the look of things."

"Maybe, but don't let it show on your face. Our best protection is to act completely innocent, even a little dumb."

They dismounted and Bill hunkered down beside the wives to admire the hide they were working on and ask if it could be bought or bartered. Minutes later Bill felt a nudge from his brother's boot.

"Here comes the chief," Dick said in a low voice.

Striding toward them was Kicking Bird and a half dozen braves. They made the ritual of welcome, first crossing their chests in the gesture of peace, then inviting the white men to sit with them in a circle and smoke the peace pipe. The pipe had just been lit when an Indian scout came dashing into camp and pulled his horse back on its haunches in front of Kicking Bird. He slid from the animal's back and joined the circle without saying a word, but he was highly agitated.

With impeccable manners, Kicking Bird waited until the peace pipe had made the circle, then he shot a single question at the scout. There came an avalanche of words and many gestures. When he finished, Kicking Bird barked a command to one of his wives who sat behind him, and she rose and padded off at a dog trot. Silence returned to the circle.

"What's going on?" Dick whispered to Bill.

"I don't know," Bill replied from the side of his mouth. "But it's something serious because the chief just sent for the medicine man."

Dick blew a soundless whistle.

The silence held until the medicine man arrived. His name was Mamanti and he was ancient and shrunken and he moved slowly, not just because of the pains in his old joints but from the dignity of power. Around his neck was hung the skin of an owl's head, and in his right hand was a fan of owl feathers. Owl medicine was the most potent of magics and employed sparingly.

Room was made for Mamanti at Kicking Bird's right, and as soon as the old man had arranged his brittle legs the chief instructed the scout to repeat his story. Again the torrent of words and the gestures but this time he added details. With three sticks he made a tripod on the dirt before him, then lay his finger at the top and seemed to sight along it. Finally he pulled from under his robe a piece of lumber about eighteen inches long. It was sharpened at one end and soiled with dirt where it had been driven into the ground. Bill recognized a surveyor's stake.

It was passed to the medicine man who studied it from all angles and finally gave his report to the chief. When he

finished speaking a heavy silence fell over the circle, broken
from time to time when Mamanti murmured the Indian
words that meant, "Bad medicine."

At last Kicking Bird turned to his guests and trans-
lated the discussion. "White men have come to our land
in wagons, but they do not hunt. They drive in stakes, but
too big for a tent. They mark where they take our hunting
land. It is bad medicine, very bad medicine."

Bill could think of nothing to say. Kicking Bird finally
said, "My people must now decide what to do about it."

"I think he wants us to leave," Bill said to his brother
and the two white men stood up. Before mounting his horse,
Bill extended his hand to Kicking Bird. The chief accepted
the white man's handshake, but he did not follow it—as was
his custom—with the sign of peace.

7

After a two-hour ride from Kicking Bird's tepee, Bill pulled
up his horse and said, "Let's make camp."

"You think it's safe here?" his brother asked.

"No place is safe any more; here or twenty miles from
here or a hundred and twenty miles. I'll stand the first
watch, you take the second."

The night was uneventful and at dawn they were again
in the saddle. They rode steadily through the day, saying
little to each other, their eyes squinted against a brassy
sun that pressed against their heads and shoulders. When
at last Bill called a halt, they unsaddled the horses and put
them to grazing, fed themselves and then stretched out in
the fragrant grass to stare at a sky gone gentle with approaching night.

"You know how long we been riding?" Dick said.

"Ten days, maybe eleven."

"And we ain't seen a buffalo."

"True enough."

"Tell me, Bill, ain't that a powerful long time to be on the
trail without seeing a single critter?"

"Yes, I reckon it is."

"You know what I'm thinking? I'm thinking the Indians
are right when they say the buffalo are being all killed off."

With great reluctance Bill said, "I'm afraid that's true."

"What happens here when they're gone?"

"I don't know."

"What are you gonna do, Bill?"

"I don't know that, neither. Except, I'm staying here. Whatever happens to this land, it'll happen to me too."

"We're different, Bill, you and me. I been in the Civil War, and now I been a buffalo hunter, and I've had all the excitement and danger I can use. Deep in me I'm a farmer. I like to make things grow. I like to get up in the morning and see the same trees and fields and valleys I saw the morning before. And I want to raise a family. I guess you can't understand."

"Sure I understand. I want those same things, but"—he raised himself on his elbow to look at the endless plain now domed with stars—"I guess I just want this more."

Silence fell between the brothers, and a sadness. At last Bill said, "When you leaving?"

"I don't know. Soon."

At dusk on the following day they made it to their base camp at Kiowa Creek. A dozen other men were there, butchers and scrapers, drivers and their teams and the flat-bed wagons used to haul the buffalo meat and hides to market. There were also three other hunters, Wright Spencer, Jim Elder and Dan Smith. These hunters had been riding north and west while the Tilghman brothers had gone south, and now they were all back together, all empty handed.

Jim Elder squinted up at Bill as he rode into camp. "You got nothin' neither. I figured if anybody could find buffalo it was you."

Bill shook his head, slid to the ground to water and feed his horse. When that was done he joined the sober-faced men who ringed the campfire.

"What do you make of it, Bill?" Wright Spencer demanded. Bill Tilghman was the youngest man there but it was his opinion they wanted.

"I don't figure to see buffalo in these parts ever again. At least, not in big enough herds to make it worth hunting."

They pondered that gloomy statement for some time. Dan Smith finally said, "Maybe up north . . ."

"I talked to a man who just come down from Dakota Territory," Spencer said. "He said that the Sioux is on the warpath. There's talk of sendin' the U. S. Army in."

"Blackfoot and Crows are warrin', too," Elder said.

"Cheyenne sure to join 'em soon," Bill added.

Spencer spit into the fire and said, "I don't mind fightin' Indians if there's buffalo to be had, but damned if I want to take a chance of bein' kilt if there's nothin' to show for it."

A murmur of agreement ran around the campfire. There seemed nothing more to be said and each man rolled himself into a blanket and went to sleep.

They were up at dawn by habit and stood about with tin cups of coffee in their hands, not knowing quite what to do next. Each man stared moodily into the bitter, dark liquid in his cup, reluctant to be the first to mount his horse and ride away. They clung together like veterans do, nostalgic for the hardship and dangers they had shared.

Jim Elder was the first to notice the rider on the rim of land to the north. As he pointed, each man eased his gun in its holster, and waited. The rider was alone, riding at a steady pace and headed for them. When he was within a few hundred yards they saw he was white and they relaxed. Silently, they sized him up. He rode well, but not well enough to be a buffalo hunter, and he carried a roll of fat around his middle which spoke of good food and soft beds. His clothes, though dusty, had not been slept in, at least not often. He wore two pistols but carried no rifle. No, he was not a hunter.

The stranger rode into camp but didn't dismount without invitation. "Howdy," he said.

"Howdy," chorused the men on the ground.

"Cup of coffee?" Jim Elder asked.

"I'd appreciate it," he said, easing himself off the horse, not without a grunt. "Been ridin' most the night."

Observing the custom of the frontier, no one asked him why he was riding, nor to where. If he wanted to tell it, he would in his own time. He accepted a cup of scalding coffee, blew on it, took a sip, then said, "I'm looking for a man named Bill Tilghman."

Again the frontier protocol was observed. It was up to Bill to announce his presence; if he didn't do so, no other man would.

"I'm Bill Tilghman."

"My name is Mart Childers."

"Yes, sir," Bill said noncommittally.

"I hear you're the best buffalo hunter in these parts. I've come to talk business."

"You're too late. Buffalo hunting's about done."

"Oh, I don't want you to hunt buffalo for me. I want you and your men to round up cattle."

"Cattle? This ain't cattle land. You gotta go south to Texas."

The man grinned. "I've come north from Texas and brought my cattle with me. Ten thousand head. Drove them up last year and let 'em graze north of the Arkansas River to fatten up. Now I want to round them up and drive them into the market at Dodge."

"Where they at, exactly?" Bill asked.

"Can't tell you, *exactly*," Childers replied. "Most the herd is still ranged along the north bank of the Arkansas, but a lot of them drifted south into Indian Territory, some as far as the Cimarron. They tell me in Dodge that you know that territory better than anybody, and you're friendly with the Indians."

Bill rubbed the back of his neck, a rueful gesture. "I

don't know any white man can claim to be friendly with the Indians nowadays."

"I'll pay you five dollars for every head you drive into Dodge."

Bill scraped up a little mound of dirt with the toe of his boot.

"Seems to me it's a fair price," Childers said. "That's what you got for buffalo, and you had to kill them, skin them and butcher them. Work for me and your five dollars walks all the way to the market on its own feet."

"All right, Mr. Childers, I'll take the job." He turned to look at his friends. "Anybody want to come along?"

"I'll go," said Jim Elder.

"Me too," said Spencer, and then Smith.

Bill avoided looking at his brother, but Dick stepped in front of him and said, "One more ride. I can be a farmer next year."

"My foreman is camped at Anderson Creek with trained cow ponies," Childers said. "When you get there he'll teach you how to herd cattle." He paused, then grinned at the men who had stiffened a bit at his words. "I know you men are good horsemen, I wouldn't be hiring you otherwise. And I ain't saying that cowpunching is harder than hunting buffalo. I'm just saying it's different, it's something a man has gotta learn. Them cattle been out there through the winter and when you get near 'em you'll find they ain't so damn docile, they're almost as wild as buffalo. And your job ain't to kill 'em, that'd be easy enough, but to drive 'em, to make 'em go where you want 'em to go. All I'm sayin' is that you'll be doin' yourselves a favor if you listen to my foreman."

"We'll listen," Bill said.

"Good," Childers exclaimed. "You men get my cattle to Dodge in good shape and you got a steady job."

Spencer spit in the dust at his feet and said, "A steady job ain't nothin' I ever hankered after."

"Maybe not, but things are gonna change around here.

The buffalo are gone, or just about gone, and cattle are gonna take their place. And I don't mean we're gonna keep drivin' 'em up from Texas, the time will come when we breed 'em and pasture 'em right here, near the railroad terminals." He made an expansive gesture. "This is gonna be the biggest damn open range in the world."

"And the Indians is gonna let you do all this?" Dan Smith asked.

"They'll let us," Childers said firmly. "The United States Army may have to come in and convince 'em, but in the end they'll let us."

The five hunters packed their gear, saddled their horses, said good-by to the stake men, the scrapers and butchers and draymen, shook hands with Childers, and rode off.

They rode many miles in silence, for they didn't want to talk about what was on their minds—Indians. Each man rode tall in the saddle, the better to see the horizon. The sun had made a little over half its daily trip when a small black smudge appeared in the sky to the west. Bill pointed it out.

"Buzzards?" Dan Smith asked.

"I reckon," Bill said.

It was several minutes before anyone spoke again. "Could be a dead buffalo," Dan Smith said.

"Or one of Childers' cows," Elder added.

"Could be," Bill agreed, "but we better have a look. They turned their horses toward the buzzards and spurred them into a gallop.

When they arrived at the charred remains of a camp, the buzzards flew into the air, crying their annoyance at the interruption. A wagon had been burned to ashes, leaving only the twisted iron fittings, springs and the rims of the wheels. A tripod for a surveyor's transit was partly burned. The horses had been driven off, but left behind were the dead and mutilated bodies of four white men.

They found a shovel with the handle only partially burned, and with it they laboriously dug four graves and filled them.

When the prairie was again smoothed over, they stood in awkward silence. "Someone ought to say a prayer," Spencer said.

"I know one," Dan Smith said. It turned out to be a child's bedtime prayer: "Now I lay me down to sleep. I pray thee, Lord, my soul to keep. If I should die before I wake, I pray thee, Lord, my soul to take."

"Amen," they all murmured together. Then they mounted and rode away.

Bill pulled his horse over beside his brother's and said quietly, "Dick, you want to turn back? Nobody is gonna think you're a coward, or anything like that. And there's a lot of good things about being a farmer."

"After what we've seen, I can't turn back. It's too late. Do you understand how I feel?"

Bill nodded. "I think I do."

8

"*Yoweeee!*" yelled Bill Martin, grabbing off his hat and slapping it against his thigh. He was nicknamed "Hurricane" for obvious reasons; he was the loudest talker, the heaviest drinker, the most reckless gambler of all the buffalo hunters on the frontier. On the other hand, he was a good shot and a responsible partner on the trail. Men liked him.

"*Yoweeee!*" he yelled again upon seeing his friend Bill Tilghman ride into Childers' base camp at Anderson Creek. "So they got you thrown and tied! Never thought I'd see the day when Bill Tilghman would turn to cow-punchin'."

"How about yourself, Hurricane?"

He made a rueful face. "Yeah, it's a sad situation. The good old days are about gone, ain't they, Bill? Well, come on into camp and meet the rest of the fellows."

Tilghman and his companions dismounted and met the foreman and a half dozen other cowboys. The foreman, making polite conversation, asked, "How was your trip?"

Jim Elder looked at Dan Smith, who looked at Wright Spencer who looked at Bill. Bill said, "The Cheyenne are on the warpath."

"I been hearin' that about one tribe or other for years," the foreman said.

"It's true now," Bill said. "We saw their work."

A hush fell on the camp as Bill told of the murdered surveyors. When the story was ended there were murmurs of anger but the foreman said coolly, "We're cattlemen, not surveyors or buffalo hunters. They'll leave us alone."

"Not likely," Bill said.

"Why not? What do they want from us?"

"They want us off the land."

"We got as much right here as them," the foreman said with some belligerence. "We ain't hurting them none. We ain't hunting, we ain't settling. We're just driving our cattle through, and by God, nobody is gonna stop us doin' that! Any man who wants out can get out . . . right now." No one moved or spoke. "All right, I figure that every one of you got a contract with me that holds until we get the cattle to Dodge."

The next day the foreman split his crew into pairs, sending each pair in a different direction. His instructions were to gather all the cattle they saw and drive them to a rendezvous point fifty miles north. To Bill and Hurricane, the best riders, he gave the responsibility of taking along the pool of extra ponies—fifteen of them.

When Bill heard that he was paired with Hurricane, he went to his brother and said, "I'm going to ask if you can ride with us."

"Why?" Dick demanded.

"Well, I . . . I don't know, I just thought you'd rather."

"What I'd *rather* is not to be treated like a tenderfoot. Don't you think I can handle this job?"

"I know you can, Dick, I just thought . . ."

"Then stop trying to mother-hen me."

Bill grinned. "I got the message."

The annual mean rainfall of the plains was around twenty inches, which isn't much unless it comes all at once—which it now did. For six days it rained; not dancing little drops but heavy sheets of water that turned placid streams into raging torrents and the prairie sod into quagmire. It was torturous going for the horses as each hoof sank ankle-deep

and had to be pulled free of the mud suction. The riders
suffered, too, for the clothes they wore were heavy with
water and rancid from the sweat and the mud they slept
upon. The flour they carried molded and had to be dis-
carded, the meat was beginning to turn. But they found
cattle all right, a half dozen here, a dozen there, and they
drove the growing herd northward through the slashing
rain.

On the morning of the eighth day the sun broke through
and began to draw up steam—from the sod, from the flanks
of the horses and cows, from the clothing the men wore.

"Which'd you rather be," Hurricane said to Bill, "boiled
in steam or drowned?"

"When I'm drowning I'd rather be boiled, and when I'm
boiling I'd rather drown."

"Yeah. I guess life ain't never exactly right for a man."

At this moment Hurricane reined up his horse and said
in a low voice, "We got another choice, Bill—being scalped."

About two miles to the south of them was a hill and
ranged on the crest of it were fifty mounted Indians. For
the moment they were motionless as they viewed the two
white men, the cattle and the horses.

"Cheyenne," Bill said. "If Kicking Bird is leading them
we might be able to parley."

"Parley, hell!" Hurricane cried. "They got their war bon-
nets on."

"Yeah, I see. But . . ."

"Damn it, Bill, them red devils is on the warpath! The
only way they'll parley is with a tomahawk."

"Kicking Bird is my friend," Bill said stubbornly.

"Not no more, he ain't. They're warring against the white
man . . . and you're white. Nothin' you nor Kicking Bird
can do about it."

"They haven't moved," Bill said hopefully.

"They will. We can't make a stand against them, not
with the odds fifty to two. We gotta run for it."

At this moment a war cry came across the plain. It

issued from fifty throats, a savage howl, a cry of vengeance, a scream of hate.

"Here they come," Hurricane said grimly.

The Indians had split into two parties, aiming to flank the white men, and were pouring down onto the plain. Bill and Hurricane spurred their horses and headed north. The thirteen extra cow ponies raced at their side.

Despite the greatest efforts by both men and horses, progress was torturous and slow. The soggy turf sucked at the horses' hoofs, making them frequently lurch and stagger. Fortunately, the Indian ponies had the same problem.

There was no talk between Bill and Hurricane, no more war cries from the Indians, all energies were devoted to the grim race of death. Slowly, slowly, the Indians began to close the gap. Bill glanced over his shoulder and tried to calculate the distance between them. If it had been two miles at the start, it was now a mile and three quarters. He spurred his horse more cruelly than he had ever done before, and the animal cried out but could run no faster.

Of the unmounted ponies running beside them, the two poorest carried packs and they were beginning to tire. Bill motioned his intention to Hurricane, who nodded in agreement. Bill pulled his hunting knife from his belt and turned his pony into the herd. With two quick slashes he cut the rope tethers that held the pack horses to the rest of the herd and they immediately slowed to a walk. Bill hoped that the horses and their packs would promise sufficient riches to lure the Indians to a halt.

Minutes later Bill looked backward to see the Indians come upon the pack horses. For a moment they swirled about them, then one of the tribe was assigned to stay behind and take them in tow while the rest of the warriors raced on after the palefaces.

It seemed to Bill that reducing the war party from fifty to forty-nine was hardly worth noting.

An hour passed, then two. Sometimes the gap widened

and sometimes narrowed. At one point Hurricane called, "They're close enough for you to pick one of 'em off."

Bill shook his head. "Killing one wouldn't do any good, and it'd just make the rest of them want revenge."

As their own mounts tired, Bill and Hurricane would rope one out of the herd, leap off for a quick change to the comparatively fresh horses. In midafternoon Hurricane was riding a large stallion named Ramrod, a fine cow horse but temperamental.

"I hate to cut him loose," Hurricane said. "He's a good horse."

"Just pity the poor Indian who gets him," Bill said.

Hurricane grinned at the idea; he knew Ramrod did not take kindly to a stranger on his back. They turned Ramrod loose and after riding on another mile, they stopped to breathe their horses and to look back. They saw the war party catch up with Ramrod, rope and saddle him. One of the Indians swung himself up on his back, and at the same moment the horse went four feet high. The Indian flew through the air as if shot from a catapult, landed on his head and lay still.

"Broke his neck, by God," Hurricane exclaimed. "Old Ramrod got one of 'em before we did."

The Indians briefly examined their fallen comrade, then resumed the chase. By four o'clock that afternoon Bill and Hurricane had changed mounts seven times and had a lead of at least four miles. It seemed that their supply of fresh mounts was going to save them. Near exhaustion but feeling the exaltation of escape, they urged their horses on.

A change now took place. The Indians divided themselves into three parties; one came down the center, while the others formed flanking parties to the left and to the right. Bill noticed it first and called out to Hurricane, "They're ridin' herd on us."

Hurricane looked back and swore bitterly. "Nothin' we can do but outrun 'em."

Minutes later they came to a hill and the Indians had
so deployed themselves that the white men could do nothing but ride straight up it. Hurricane was in the lead and
when he came to the top, pulled his horse back on its
haunches. He turned toward Bill, his face white and set.

"They sure enough trapped us," he said.

Bill spurred his horse up the few remaining yards to the
summit, then reined in just in time to save himself from
plunging over a cliff. There was an almost sheer drop of
sixty feet to a stream that was swollen and rampaging from
the recent rains. Bill dismounted to steady his nervous horse.
He looked to the east and then to the west, but the flanking war parties cut off escape in either direction, and the
main party was thundering straight at them.

Hurricane let out a stream of oaths, ending querulously,
"And we let them do it . . . we let them drive us right
into the trap!"

Bill removed his lariat from the saddle and slipped the
main loop over his horse's head.

Hurricane said, "We better kill our horses and use their
bodies for barricades. It'll give us more time."

"How much more time?" Bill asked.

Hurricane shrugged. "Until our ammunition runs out."

"And then?" Bill demanded, forcing Hurricane to say
the worst.

"I think you know," Hurricane said.

The memory of the scalped and mutilated surveyors
came to Bill's mind. Horror and fear and anger churned
in his stomach and he felt sick.

The flanking war parties had changed their angle of approach, both bending inward to meet the main party at the
foot of the hill. As the trap slowly closed, the Indians began
to scream.

Hurricane dismounted and said, quite calmly, "Be sure
to save your last bullet for yourself." He pulled his pistol
and aimed it at his horse's head.

"Don't do that," Bill said sharply. "We'll need him. We're going over the cliff."

"Over the cliff? You crazy? We'd break our necks."

"We might, but we might not. Besides, we got no choice."

Bill led his pony to the edge of the cliff, then smacked him on the rump, but the animal braced himself stiff-legged and refused to move. "Ride into him, Hurricane. Bump him over. Hurry!"

Leaping on his horse, Hurricane drove him against the pony. For a moment the pony seemed able to suspend himself in mid-air. Then, screaming, his hoofs working furiously, he dropped from view. The two men threw themselves on their bellies at the lip of the precipice and stared down. The sheer drop was for about half the distance down, some forty feet, then there was a more gradual sloping outward toward the stream. The pony hit the slope on his side with a loud thud and a rasping gasp of pain, then it rolled and tumbled to the edge of the stream, where it lay still.

"Jesus!" Hurricane breathed. "Must have broke every bone in his body.

There floated up to them a pitiful whinny of pain and bewilderment. Then the pony climbed to its feet. It trembled, but it stood.

"I'll go next," Bill said. "Can you get your horse over alone?"

"I'll blindfold him."

Bill eased himself over the lip, clung to it for a moment with his fingertips, then let go. Almost instantly, it seemed, the earth came up to hit him, jackknifing his legs, driving his knees into his stomach, knocking the wind out of him. He gagged for air. Above him the sky spun while the earth heaved and attacked. There seemed no end to the torture and he must have cried out, but he could hear nothing.

Suddenly his head was very cold and his ears seemed filled with water. He raised his head to find he was lying in the edge of the stream, and nearby was his horse, the lariat still around its neck. He checked his own arms and

legs and found they could move. He grabbed the end of
the rope and entered the stream. The boiling current knocked
him from his feet, but the horse was his anchor and he
was not swept downstream. Choking and sputtering, he got
his feet under him and braced against the water that pulled
at him. He was in the middle now, where the current was
swiftest, and if only he could make another few steps into the
shallower water, he'd be safe.

His horse made it to shore ahead of him, and by the rope
pulled him to safety. He lay on the ground, barely conscious.

As his senses returned he saw Hurricane lying on the
ground nearby, and beyond him stood the two horses, their
heads down and their sides heaving. He looked at the cliff
towering above him. There were no Indians looking down
from the summit . . . not yet.

He called to Hurricane, who groaned, "Mother of God!"

"Hurricane, we gotta move out. We're perfect targets
here."

It was almost beyond their strength to mount, and having
done so, it was beyond the horses' strength to move faster
than a walk. When they had gone a hundred yards Bill
looked back. On the rim of the cliff, silhouetted against
the sky, was a line of Indians on horseback. Bill pulled up
his gun and snapped a shot in their direction. They immediately slid from their horses and flattened themselves
on the ground. They did not return the fire, nor did they
come down the cliff. The chase was done.

Early the following morning Bill pointed out a dust cloud
on the horizon. "A big herd," he said. "Should be cattle—
Childers' cattle."

Of the Childers crew, Jim Elder was the first to spot
them and he came galloping their way. "We begun to worry
about you," he called.

Hurricane grinned. "We been doin' a bit of worryin',
too. Any booze in camp?"

"I think Cookie's got some stashed away in the chuck wagon."

"*Yoweee!*" Hurricane cried, galloping toward the distant wagon.

Elder brought his horse alongside Bill's. "Indians?"

"Yeah," Bill replied.

"Bill, I got some bad news for you."

The young man stiffened, for he guessed what it was. "My brother?"

"Yeah. I'm sorry."

"How'd it happen?"

"Dick got separated and lost. Didn't make camp last night. We set to searching at dawn, found his body. The Indians . . ." He didn't finish the sentence.

"You buried him?" Bill finally asked.

"No, figured you might want to do that. His body's in the tool wagon." As Bill put spurs to his horse, Elder called, "If I was you I wouldn't unwrap him."

When the drive resumed, Bill drove the tool wagon and looked for a grave site. He delayed the decision for several hours while the rest of the crew rode at a distance to give him privacy for his thoughts.

He thought he hated the Indians, but he discovered it was an incomplete hate. He didn't hate Kicking Bird or Little Robe or White Deer or Sleeping Elk or Standing Bear or any of the Indians he knew. He hated the strangers, the ones who had killed his brother.

Late in the afternoon they came upon a rocky meadow and Bill decided this was the place. The cattle rested and grazed while all hands helped dig the deep grave. Bill gathered his brother's shrouded body in his arms and lowered it tenderly into the ground. He turned away while the rest of them filled the grave and then piled rocks on top of it to discourage the wolves. Then they all rode on.

9

Despite the hazards of the trail, Childers' herd of Texas longhorns numbered close to nine thousand head when it was driven into the cattle pens beside the railroad at Dodge City.

The town took on a carnival atmosphere because there was to be money for everybody. Childers received money selling his herd to packers; the railroad freight representative received money for providing cattle cars and transportation east; the cowboys received money for the long and dangerous job just completed, and upon the cowboys the town's commerce fattened. Saloonkeepers, gamblers, madams and misses, they all shared the cowboys' pay—and quickly. In fact, the average cowboy held his money so briefly that it didn't seem to belong to him at all; he seemed merely a transfer agent for it.

Childers paid off his men one at a time and when he came to Bill Tilghman he said, "You got the makings of a good cowman, son. How'd you like to come down to Texas and work for me, steady?"

Bill gave the offer a decent moment of thought, then said, "I guess not. Though I thank you."

"Oh, I know you got a big reputation as a buffalo hunter, but, kid, those days are gone. You got no trade left, unless"—he pointed derisively to a great pile of bones stacked by a railway siding—"unless you're gonna be a Stinker."

Buffalo hunters had frequently shot more animals than they could butcher, and the carcasses littered the plain, freezing in winter, thawing and decomposing in summer. When there developed a market for bones (to be ground into fertilizer) any man with a wagon and a team could drive into the old hunting grounds, cut the bones out of the decaying flesh, and deliver them to Dodge at eight dollars a ton. Since they inevitably took on the odor of their work, these men became known as Stinkers. They called themselves bone haulers, but the citizens of Dodge called them Stinkers.

Bill grinned at Childers and said, "No, I don't plan to become a Stinker."

"Well, what are you gonna do?"

"Right now I don't know. But one day I'm gonna be a lawman."

"A lawman!"

"Yes, sir."

"All the sheriffs I've known just kinda drifted into the job. I never heard of a man planning it ahead of time. It must be you just like to live dangerous."

"Maybe that's part of it," Bill grinned.

Childers counted the dollars into his hand, then warned, "Don't let this town take all your money from you."

"I don't aim to let that happen."

As they shook hands, Childers said, "If you change your mind, come on down to Texas. They'll always be a job for you."

After the pay-off Bill found himself swept up with his celebrating friends and was soon bellied up to a bar. The saloon was a large, bleak room made of raw lumber with beams and rafters showing. The bar itself was an enormous plank nailed to sawhorses. The air was stagnant with the odors of sweat and beer laced with the bitter spice of cheap whiskey. No effort had been made by the owner to decorate the room, to soften or conceal the ugliness, for it was his opinion that "fancy trimmin's don't sell one extra glass of whiskey."

"What'll ya have?" Hurricane asked Bill.

Tilghman thought a moment while the bartender attended. "I'd like a lemonade," he finally announced.

"Lemonade?" Hurricane said in a disbelieving voice.

"Yeah, if it's not too much trouble."

"Look, kid," his friend said, "you didn't take a drink durin' the drive, and I could understand not wantin' to hit the saddle in the morning with a red-hot head that tries to explode with every step your pony takes. But that's all over. We ain't workin' tomorrow. This is the time to hoot it up. Take a drink."

"I just don't like the taste of the stuff, Hurricane."

"Who does?" Hurricane made a scornful gesture toward the bottles of whiskey stacked on the back bar. "Nobody likes the taste of the rotgut they sell here, but it does the job. It puts a rainbow around you."

"I've seen it put storm clouds around some men."

"The mean ones, sure. But we ain't mean, Bill. We're out for a little fun. Don't blue-nose it."

Tilghman slapped his friend on the back. "You get as drunk as you want to, Hurricane, I don't mind. But I have more fun when I'm sober, when I know what's going on."

Conversation had stopped all up and down the bar and a line of faces turned toward Tilghman. There were no insults, no derision, the young man's prowess as horseman and hunter were well known and no man wished to challenge him. If the order for lemonade had come from an Eastern dude they would have bent double, choking on their own laughter. They would have pounded each other on the back and shouted their opinions of his manhood, speculated on his method of urinating. But when this weathered young hunter ordered lemonade they could find no fun in it, only mystery, and they stared at him in dumb disbelief.

Finally one man muttered to his neighbor, "Iffen he ain't gonna drink, what's he come into the saloon fer?"

"Beats me," the other replied.

A man coming off the trail and looking for relaxation and human companionship could go to a bawdy house, a gambling parlor or a saloon. Bill chose the saloon. He was not there to censor or belittle but, like the rest of them, was simply trying to shed the trail loneliness. When this was understood, he was accepted.

After several days he was more than accepted, he was welcomed. He played a role in the saloon society, he was an arbitrator. Men twice his age would turn to him for the settlement of whiskey-inflamed arguments. He never gave an opinion unless asked, and then without pridefulness. If his statement was challenged he refused to argue the point, merely saying, "Well, that's the way I see it." In most instances this simple statement ended all contention.

"I hear there's a dance tonight at Sun City," Hurricane informed Bill one Saturday. "Let's go give it a whirl."

Sun City was seventy-five miles southeast of Dodge, but it wasn't the distance that made Bill hesitate. "I don't dance very good," he said.

"You got two feet, ain't you? And you can move 'em, can't you?"

"I suppose."

"Well, that's good enough excuse to take a girl in your arms."

"I dunno, Hurricane. I'm afraid I'd step on her toes."

"That's her lookout. She's jest gotta be quick enough to keep her toes out from under yer boots. Dammit, Bill, you don't drink but you're sure as hell gonna dance with a girl— if I have to tie you and throw you over your saddle."

It was purple twilight when the two riders came out of the plains and headed toward a cluster of unpainted wooden buildings that bore the name of SUN CITY. The riders were tired and dusty but as they entered the rutted main street they heard a sound that quickened their pulses—the staccato thump of a banjo, the headlong cry of a fiddle, and an occasional peal of girlish laughter.

The music and laughter spilled out of a vacant store building which, for the occasion, was filled with the golden light of a dozen lanterns. In front of the store was a number of young men who lounged about, kicking the dirt and indulging in loud male talk. Since they had not yet worked up the courage to enter the dance hall, they pretended it didn't exist.

Hurricane and Bill hitched their horses, then walked to the rear of the building where the hospitality committee had placed a bucket of water, a tin washbasin, a chip of soap and a towel. After they had washed their faces and hands, Hurricane removed a small jar from his pocket and unscrewed the lid to reveal a thick substance which he dipped out with two fingers and rubbed into his hair.

"Want some?" He offered the jar. "It's pomade."

A pungent flower odor came to Bill and he stepped back from the proffered jar. "I don't want that on me. It smells."

"That's the idee," Hurricane said. "Ya smell anyway, but with this you smell good."

"No, thanks," Bill said firmly.

Hurricane shrugged his shoulders, returned the pomade jar to his pocket, removed a comb and worked his hair until it was flat against his skull and glistened as if varnished. Then putting on a swagger, he led Bill around to the front of the building and into the room.

The whole town had turned out for the dance and there were round dances and square dances being performed with happy gusto by oldsters and youngsters alike. Just inside the door was the stag line, young men who had found sufficient courage to enter the room but not enough to carry them on to the cluster of young ladies on the far side. Hurricane cut boldly across the floor but Bill only made it about halfway. Suddenly every eye was on him, he was certain, and he turned and bolted for the safety of the stag line.

Moments later he beheld a terrifying scene. Hurricane

was coming back across the floor with *two* girls. "Oh, Lord, he's got one for me," Bill groaned inwardly. "What am I gonna do?"

"Bill," Hurricane called, "stop trying to hide. I got you a pardner."

"I wasn't trying to hide," Bill said, his face scarlet.

"I want you to meet Miss Flora Kendall and Miss Mollie Tilden," Hurricane said. "And, ladies, this big galoot with his mouth open is Bill Tilghman, the famous buffalo hunter and Indian fighter."

"Aw, cut it out, Hurricane."

"Pleased to meet you," both girls murmured demurely.

"I'm havin' this dance with Miss Mollie, so you take Miss Flora."

And before Bill could turn to flee, the young lady stepped forward and stood expectantly not more than twelve inches from him. There was simply nothing he could do but put his arm around her waist and begin to dance.

Never had he known such soul agony. His feet seemed to be made of lead and it was beyond his strength to do more than shuffle them slowly, a few inches at a time. There was a roaring in his head that drowned out the sound of music. His mouth was dry and his teeth locked together. His mind was occupied with the horrible certainty that he would soon step on this fragile creature he held in his arms.

After some moments he dared believe that he'd get through the dance without disaster and he allowed himself to look down at her. He saw an oval face topped by clusters of brown curls. Wide-set brown eyes stared directly into his own, and on her lips was the shadow of a smile.

She was obviously waiting for him to start a conversation, and again panic hit him. He could think of nothing to say, not a single topic, not a single word. The very language seemed to have drained from his mind. He lifted his chin and for the remainder of the dance looked straight over her head.

"Thank you very much, Mr. Tilghman," she said sweetly when the dance ended.

Bill opened his mouth and a squeak came out of it. Flora had no idea what word was intended. Nor did Bill. They stood there at an impasse until Hurricane came to announce, "Bill, you got the next dance with Miss Mollie."

The fiddle and banjo players had wiped their faces and necks with red bandannas, refreshed themselves with long drafts of some unidentified liquid contained in a brown jug, and now struck up a tune with even more vigor than before.

Mollie was blonde and vivacious and full of chatter. She relieved Bill of the responsibility to talk, she even made him forget his leaden feet. He danced with her four times during the rest of the evening.

A bright half-moon hung above Bill and Hurricane as they started back for Dodge shortly after midnight. They walked their horses for a time, listening to the rhythmic clop of the hoofs, the only sound on the vast, moonwashed plain.

Bill at last broke the silence. "When they gonna hold another dance?"

Hurricane snorted. "You mean that next time I ain't gonna have to practically tie ya into the saddle to get ya here?"

"Nope," sheepishly. After a long pause, "She's a real nice girl."

"I could see you was smitten," Hurricane chuckled.

"You could? Really?"

"A guy don't dance with a girl four times in a row unless he's got some interest in her. And I don't blame ya. That Mollie is a corker."

"Mollie? No, I'm talking about Flora."

"Flora! You mean the first girl? The one you danced with only once? The one you couldn't wait to get free of?" Hurricane turned in the saddle to face his friend. "Flora was the one you was interested in, so you ignored her all evening. Is that what you're tellin' me?"

"I guess it is, Hurricane."

"What in hell made you act that way?"

"I dunno. I just couldn't get myself to ask her for another dance, much as I wanted to. What do you suppose Flora is thinkin' about me?"

"I dunno, but I can tell you what she should be thinkin'— that you're a damn fool."

Bill sighed heavily. "I guess that's about right."

The violence of the Indian wars was increasing. President Ulysses S. Grant believed (not surprisingly) that the United States Army could solve almost any problem, and he committed more and more troops to the plains. One of the principal military staging areas was Dodge and the saloons and bordellos were filled with men in blue uniforms. Since most of the soldiers, officers and enlisted men were from the East and had no idea of what awaited them on the plains, experienced guides were in great demand. The man whose reputation towered above all others was Bill Tilghman and he was constantly courted by colonels and brigadiers.

Tilghman politely declined the offers, saying that he had other plans; which, indeed, he did. In the years ahead he was to undertake more projects than any five men. He became a merchant, rancher, contractor, land speculator, horse racer, fair manager, entertainment entrepreneur, politician, and even saloonkeeper. Such an ambitious man, however benign in face and manner, was certain to make enemies.

In February 1878 the Dodge City *Times* reported: "Wm. Tilghman . . . was arrested on the . . . serious charge of attempt to rob . . . (a) train. He stated that he was ready for trial, but the State asked for ten days delay to procure witnesses, which was granted. Tilghman gave bail. It is generally believed that Wm. Tilghman had no hand in the attempted robbery."

At the end of ten days Tilghman was released and even received a letter of apology from the officials. The *Times* printed the letter: "Dear sir—your case was called today for examination. There being no evidence against you, I filed a motion for your discharge . . . I congratulate you on your discharge, hoping that you may be so lucky in the future as not to be ever suspected of crime. Yours very truly, J. E. McArthur, County Attorney, Edwards County, Kansas."

Back in 1876, however, his plan was not about his business or public career, but something closer to his heart. It was the sort of thing a man would tell to only his closest friend. In this case it was Hurricane.

But immediately after their visit to Sun City, Hurricane had gone back to cowpunching. He was on the trail for three months. Finally returning to Dodge, he set about looking for Tilghman, came upon him in the dusty street and wrapped him in a bear hug.

"They tell me you been busy these last months," Hurricane said.

"Yeah, I been busy," Bill grinned.

"But nobody seems to know what you been busy about. You ain't been seen around town much. What's the mystery?"

"No mystery."

"You found gold?"

"Nothing like that."

"Well, if you don't want to tell me, I ain't gonna pry."

"I always meant to tell you, Hurricane, but you been away driving cattle for months. Come on, let's get our horses and I'll show you."

They rode out of town to the south and west and an hour later breasted a rise to look down on Bluff Creek. Where the creek made a sharp bend there were several buildings—a dugout dwelling, two sheds and a corral. Grazing nearby was a small herd of cattle.

"That's mine," Bill announced.

Hurricane's jaw dropped in disbelief. "You . . . you homesteaded?"

Under the Homestead Act at the end of the Civil War, any

man could claim 160 acres of public land for a nominal fee, receiving full title at the end of five years if he worked or improved the land.

"A homesteader!" Hurricane repeated dolefully. "I never figured you for a farmer."

"I grew up on a farm."

"You couldn't help yourself as a young 'un. But now . . ." His voice trailed off, he couldn't find the words to express his disappointment that a free man should voluntarily become domesticated. Then a new thought came to Hurricane's mind, a thought that would excuse his friend for what he had done. "I'll bet it's a woman that drove you to this, Bill. You'd never do something like this if you was in your right mind. It's gotta be a woman who's fevered you up. God dammit, I should've made you go with me on this last drive and you wouldn't have got in trouble." He gave a heavy sigh. "Who's the woman ya gettin' hitched to?"

"I haven't asked her yet, but . . . well, it's Flora Kendall I have in mind."

"That gal in Sun City? You seen her since that dance?"

"No, but I wrote her a couple of letters, friendly letters."

Hurricane shook his head. "On the basis of one dance and two letters you sure went to a hell of a lot of trouble."

"Now that I got everything fixed up I plan on riding over next week and ask her."

It was the following day that Tilghman came upon an old friend he hadn't seen for quite a time, a cowhand named Joe Robinson. "Good to see you, Joe," he said warmly. "What's new with you?"

"Well, the biggest news is I got myself hitched. Married the prettiest little thing in the whole territory. Sun City gal named Flora. Flora Kendall."

Six months later Joe Robinson was dead. During a roundup his horse stumbled and fell on top of him, breaking his neck. When Bill heard that the widow was destitute,

he brought her and her unborn baby to Dodge and paid her
board and room with an elderly couple. He waited a year
before asking her to marry him. She said yes and they moved
onto his Bluff Creek ranch the spring of 1877.

10

Bill and Flora worked from sunup to sundown through that first summer and their small ranch was as groomed as any in the territory. Flora was totally happy. She had a home and a child (a second on the way) and a strong, gentle husband. The world was big, she knew, but this 160 acres was all of it she desired.

There was one small cloud in her life, her husband seemed restless. Even after fourteen hours of the hard physical labor he would spend the twilight hour pacing around the corral. She had not the experience to read the symptoms, she assumed that all men liked a certain amount of privacy, and she did not intrude.

During a September sunset Bill sat on his corral fence and squinted to the east where a lone rider was headed toward him at full gallop. As the rider reined his horse with a flourish, Bill recognized the famous buffalo hunter, guide, Indian fighter, poker player and gunfighter, Bat Masterson. Each man threw up his arm in greeting, then Masterson dismounted, hitched his horse, seated himself on the corral fence, took out a sack of tobacco and thin papers and began to roll a cigarette—all in silence.

These two men were friends, though quite unlike. Masterson was flamboyant in dress and manner. Strangers asking after Masterson were frequently told, "The best dressed man in the saloon will be Masterson." He had recently begun wearing the Mexican vaquero's pants, cut wide and elaborately embroidered. Around his waist was a brightly colored sash, and over that he wore a velvet jacket. Normally such dandyism would have called for hoots of derision, but not when it was Masterson. To the time he sat on the corral with Bill Tilghman he was credited with killing twenty-seven men. Masterson would point out in all modesty that at least half of them were Indians who didn't really count.

After his cigarette was lighted, Masterson came to the point: "The boys in Dodge want me to run for county sheriff this fall."

Bill hoped that the surprise he felt did not show on his face. It must have, for Masterson grinned at him and said, "I guess you never figured me for a lawman, huh? Well, I didn't neither until now. Things have changed. Dodge ain't a frontier town any longer, it's got churches and stores and respectable women and little children. Every time a bunch of liquored-up cowhands ride into town on a Saturday night to shoot it up, they hurt innocent people. The merchants want this stopped. They don't want the saloons closed down, they want the cowpunchers to come in on Saturday nights and spend their money, but they want the gunplay stopped. They seem to think I'm the man that can do it."

"I reckon they're right about that," Bill said.

"I'll need some help, Bill. That's why I rode out here to see you. If I'm elected, will you be my under-sheriff?"

"Yes, sir," Bill said promptly. "I will."

Bat Masterson was elected and took office on January 1, 1878. Bill Tilghman put a hired hand on his ranch, moved his family to Dodge City, and became under-sheriff. The first day on the job, Masterson tilted his chair against the wall and studied Tilghman.

"Bill, I hear you're a real fast draw. That so?"

"Pretty fast. I been practicing a lot."

"Think you can outdraw me?"

"I don't know," Bill grinned. "Hope I never have to find out."

After a moment of further study, Masterson said, "You won't take a drink, they tell me."

"That's right."

"Well, I do. And I don't see nothin' wrong with a cow-puncher gettin' drunk on a Saturday night as long as he don't pull a gun."

"I agree," Bill said.

"What I'm sayin' is, I don't want you to arrest a man just because he's drunk."

Bill nodded his head, but Masterson continued to stare at him with some perplexity. "Why the hell is it you won't take a drink, Bill?"

"I've seen a number of gunfights between a drunk man and a sober man—the sober man always won. His reflexes are faster, his aim steadier. If I have to get in a gunfight, I want that advantage."

"I suppose you're right," Masterson said, "but it's sure a hell of a way to go through life, sober all the time."

"You get used to it," Bill grinned.

Masterson waved his hand. "Bill, go out and tour the town. Visit every whorehouse, every saloon, every store. You're well known around here but I want the town to see you with that badge on your vest. I want this town to know that when you and I walk into a saloon we're the law. Let's not have anybody confused about that. Can save a lot of trouble."

Bill nodded. "I don't expect much trouble during day-light."

"Can't count on that any more. There's a lot of bad blood in this town. The cowboy on a Saturday-night drunk, he's no problem. Take his gun away and he turns real peaceable. No, the bad blood I'm talking about is between cattlemen and sheepmen; between cattlemen and farmers; between farmers and sheepmen. There's whites who hates Indians real bad and gun 'em down whenever they get an excuse. And there's trouble between the Indians and the Mexicans; between the Mexicans and the whites. Some men are still fighting the Civil War. You get Confederates from Texas and Union men from Kansas, get 'em in the same saloon and you're bound to have trouble. As for women, well, they're kinda in short supply—I mean the respectable ones—and there's been some shootin' over them."

"I didn't realize . . ." Bill began.

"You look at a town different when you're a sheriff. You see a lot of things other men don't see." He waved his hand. "Go on out there and have a look."

Bill stepped out of the office and began strolling down the street. The town *did* look different to him now that he had a responsibility for it. For the first time he noticed where the alleys and vacant lots were—possible places of concealment. He studied the porches and roofs from which a man might control the street. He tried to catalog each building according to the kind of trouble it might produce.

The town was built along both sides of the Santa Fe railroad track, and the main street which ran parallel to the track was called Front Street. The track not only brought a train to town once a day, it served to divide Dodge into good and bad neighborhoods. South of the tracks ("the wrong side of the tracks") were the bawdy houses, the cheaper saloons, and Boot Hill which contained the shallow graves of gunmen who died with their boots on.

On the north side of the tracks were the better saloons and gambling houses, a hotel named the Dodge House, the Ford County Courthouse, the volunteer fire company, and a vaudeville theater named Variety. Also, a family cemetery whose tenants had died from causes other than gunshot wounds. There was a roofed-over boardwalk on the north side where ladies and gentlemen might walk from hotel to theater without soiling their shoes in the dirt.

As he walked down Front Street, seeing the town with new eyes, Bill was surprised at how many elegantly dressed men and women thronged the street. There was a simple explanation: nearly half the town's population were gamblers and prostitutes. Satins and bows, velvets and brocades were the uniform of their trades.

Scattered here and there among the gaudy people was the drab raiment of cowboys still dusty from the trail; the shapeless, ankle-length calico dresses of farm women whose faces were weathered beyond their years; a few "Eastern dudes" who wore black four-button suits and high paper collars.

As Bill moved down the street he was frequently hailed: "Hi there, Sheriff."

"You put anybody in jail yet, Bill?"

"When you gonna clean up the town, Sheriff?"

"You got the bad men on the run?"

Bill answered with a grin and a wave of his hand. He knew he was being kidded, tested, and how he responded would set his relationship with the town for months to come. And so he moved slowly through the crowds, grinning at the verbal barbs, modestly accepting the congratulations.

"The kid seems okay," was the general comment. But the town planned a little more testing.

It was mid-afternoon by the time Bill had worked his way through Dodge and to the railway depot and the cattle pens on the edge of town. He sat with the freight agent and they talked about old times when buffalo hides were stacked by the hundred along this same platform. It had been only a few short years before, but it was gone so completely it already seemed like ancient history.

When they ran out of talk they were content to sit a while in silence. Bill came abruptly out of his reverie at the sound of gunfire. He looked at the freight agent to confirm the direction, it was back in town, and he jumped up and ran for Front Street. He found a lone man walking slowly down the middle of the dusty road. Then an astounding thing happened—a frock-coated figure ran out from the boardwalk directly up to the man in the road, leveled a gun at his head and fired. A moment later another man did the same thing, aimed directly at the victim's head and fired. This happened four times while Bill sprinted down the road. The scene was something out of a nightmare, for the man being shot continued walking.

When Bill raced up to him, his own gun in hand, the man gave him a raffish grin and said, "Afternoon, Sheriff. Caught yerself any bad men, yet?"

Only then did Bill recognize the man; it was Luke Short, operator of the Red Dog Saloon. Bill stammered, "I thought you was shot up."

"Not me, just my hat."

He pointed toward the tall plug hat he was wearing, now full of bullet holes. It was one of Dodge City's traditions that no man was allowed to wear a plug hat within the city limits. Whenever an Easterner appeared in town wearing such a hat, it was shot off his head.

"We just made a little bet, that's all. The boys bet me I couldn't walk a block without my hat being knocked off. Well, it ain't knocked off, is it, Sheriff? Full of bullet holes but it's still on my head. Looks like I won the bet, wouldn't you say, Sheriff?"

Bill didn't know what to do, or what to say, and so he stood dumb. Luke became solicitous, full of mock concern.

"Sheriff, you figure a crime's been committed? You figurin' on arrestin' somebody? Well, I can tell you, there's a lot of bad men right over there." He pointed to the board sidewalk where a half dozen men lounged and smirked. Among them Bill recognized several of Luke's cronies. There was Wyatt Earp, a Texas cowboy who spent more time in saloons than he did in the saddle. There was stocky Ben Thompson, a printer by trade, a gunfighter by temperament. He was credited with killing thirty-two men, some of them by knife. Also there was the immaculately groomed but consumptive dentist, "Doc" Holliday. He had given up dentistry for whiskey and gambling. His sandy mustache was carefully groomed in the drooping style of the day, his blond hair was meticulously combed, his fingernails trimmed and clean. He looked like a medical man, germfree and competent, until one got close enough to discover that his blue eyes were totally without expression. Up until this day he had killed twenty-six men; his lifetime record was to be thirty.

These were the men toward whom Luke Short gestured. "There's some bad ones there, Sheriff. Think you can put 'em in jail?"

Bill knew now that this little drama had been played for his benefit, to make him look ridiculous. Well, it had accomplished that, all right. There he stood in the middle of the street, his gun in his hand and no place to aim it.

"What you gonna do, Sheriff?" Luke simpered. "Who you gonna shoot?"

His face crimson, Bill jammed his gun back in its holster and marched on down the street, mocking laughter following him.

Later that afternoon, when he reported back to the office, he found Masterson with his feet on the desk and a bemused expression on his face. "How'd it go, Bill?"

"All right."

"No gunplay?"

"Nothing worth mentioning."

"You didn't arrest nobody for shooting Luke's hat full of holes?" Masterson tilted back his head and brayed his laughter. "You gotta expect a little raggin', Bill. But I'll tell the boys to lay off."

"You don't have to on my account. Besides, I learned something this afternoon."

"Yeah?"

"I'm never again going to pull my gun unless I have to . . . unless I mean to use it."

Masterson rubbed his chin. "A good resolution, Bill, but a damned hard one to keep."

"I'll keep it," Bill said.

Dodge's reputation as a wicked city attracted the unsavory, to be sure, but also those who hoped to "save" the town—itinerant preachers and revivalists. Since no church had yet been built, the revival meetings were held in whatever vacant store was available, frequently one sandwiched between saloons and bawdy houses. At least the preachers were bringing their messages where they were most needed.

Tilghman had been on the job about a week when "Salvation Sam" walked into his office to announce his intention of holding a revival meeting that night. Tilghman took note of the store in which it would be held and then nodded his permission.

"Sheriff, you been saved?" Salvation Sam demanded.

"Well, Reverend, I'm not certain I've ever been lost."

"All men are born to sin," Salvation Sam declared in his doomsday voice. "All men must confess, there can be no salvation without public confession. You must be cleansed, brother, before you can be reborn. Come to the meeting tonight, Sheriff. For your soul's sake come and hear the Word of God."

"Thank you, Reverend. I'll give it some thought."

Tilghman was to attend, all right, but not in the manner either of them could have anticipated.

It was about nine o'clock that night when the muffled sound of gunfire reverberated down Front Street and into the sheriff's office. Bill was alone, working on the department's records—the number of prisoners in custody, the cost of their feeding, charges against them, disposition by the court. As under-sheriff it was his job to take care of all the routine paperwork, as well as assisting Mike Sutton, County Prosecutor, in preparing the cases for trial.

At the sound of the shots he went outside and began to walk briskly down Front Street. He could usually spot the place of the trouble by the actions of the citizens. If the shooting was in the street, everyone took refuge indoors; if the gunplay was indoors, everyone poured into the street. As he looked now he saw a cluster of men and women on the boardwalk a few doors west of the Red Dog Saloon.

The crowd opened to let him through. There were no

taunts, no mocking him now that danger was present. "The shootin's in there," several informed him, "right where the preacher were savin' souls." Bill headed toward the door when a voice called out, "Watch yourself, Sheriff. That's Mysterious Dave in there doin' the shootin'."

Bill nodded his thanks for the warning and entered the building. Inside there were wooden benches set in rows before a large, rough lectern. Behind the lectern there crouched a dozen men and women seeking refuge from the bullets. On one side of the room, gun in hand, stood "Mysterious Dave" Mather. Slowly he turned his gun from the direction of the lectern and aimed it at the sheriff.

Above the gun was a closed face. There seemed no flesh on it, merely yellowed skin stretched tight over chin and cheekbones. No lips were visible, a straight slash formed the mouth, and the eyes were set so deep, were so shadowed by the craggy skull that one couldn't be certain where they looked.

Dodge citizens had labeled him "Mysterious Dave" not only because of the remoteness of his face but also the spareness of his conversation. About once a month he would ride in from the plains, plant himself at the end of a bar and get quietly drunk. At least, everyone assumed he got drunk by the amount of whiskey he consumed. There were no other signs, no softening of expression, no volubility, no stagger to his walk. He simply poured a quart of whiskey down his throat, then moved with stately gait to his tethered horse, mounted with no difficulty and rode back into the plains to disappear for another month.

The bully boys in Dodge left Mysterious Dave strictly alone. His silences seemed to make him formidable, and not knowing what to expect from him, they didn't stir him up. Now, with the shooting up of the revival meeting, they nodded their heads and said they had known all the time that he was a gun fighter.

Bill Tilghman and Mysterious Dave stared at each other across the silent room. "I want you to give me your gun,

Dave," Bill said. There was no response, not even the blink of an eyelid. Bill began walking slowly toward him. "I'm not going to hurt you, Dave, I just want your gun so you don't hurt anybody either."

With his chest inches from the gun barrel, Bill stopped and extended his hand. "Give me your gun, Dave." Slowly it was done. Bill stuck the gun in his waistband, then called over his shoulder, "Anybody hurt?"

There was a murmur of denial as the preacher and his flock came out from behind the lectern.

"Reverend, you'll have to come with me to make out charges against this man."

"I'll make no charges."

"Are you sure you don't want to?"

The preacher pointed a trembling finger toward the sky. "Charges against this sinner have been made in heaven. God will punish him as He sees fit."

Tilghman nodded and took Mysterious Dave's arm to lead him away. At the door, Dave turned toward the disconcerted worshipers and spat out a single word: "Hypocrites!"

Back at the office Bill said, "Now tell me what happened."

Mysterious Dave looked at the wall for a time, then said, "They's hypocrites." The sheriff nodded and waited patiently for more. "The preacher asked them to come forward and confess their sins. They done it and then the preacher said they was now pure and could go straight to heaven. I figgered to help 'em along on the trip, get 'em to heaven while their souls was still clean and they was sure to get in." His mouth curled in disdain. "Turned out they didn't want to go to heaven at all. Hypocrites."

Tilghman stood up and said, "Here's your gun. I'll ride with you to the edge of town."

The two men walked their horses to the town's western limit where the prairie began its endless run into the night. Tilghman said, "Dave, don't come back to Dodge. You left some bad blood here, men who think it's pretty low to shoot at an unarmed minister and a bunch of women. If you come back, somebody is sure to challenge you and you'll end up either dead or in jail."

Mysterious Dave gave no indication that he heard Tilghman's words, but he was never again seen in Dodge.

II

Dodge City slowly learned that she had a new kind of sheriff in Bill Tilghman. Frontier towns were accustomed to flashy men like Bat Masterson and Wyatt Earp, men who were fearless and quick on the gun, who considered themselves not only sheriff, but also judge and jury, and whose verdicts were frequently delivered with bullets. These men were only half law; the other half was outlaw.

Bill Tilghman was a different stamp of man. He was quiet-spoken, reluctant to pull his gun, and he seemed concerned what the *law* was, those things written in books. Shortly after his appointment as under-sheriff he made a call on Mike Sutton, the County Prosecutor.

"Mr. Sutton," he said, "I'd be obliged to you if you'd teach me the law."

The attorney looked at him in surprise, then waved his hand at the bookshelf along one wall. "There's the law, fifty volumes, and that's only part of it."

"Oh, I didn't mean I wanted to know it all, just the things that apply to my job. Misdemeanors and felonies and things like that."

"Oh," Sutton said, still puzzled.

"The way I see it, I've got no right to arrest a man because I don't like his looks, or because somebody else doesn't like his looks. The only reason for an arrest should be that he's breaking the law. So I've gotta know what the law is."

"I'll be damned," Sutton said, shaking his head. "You're the first sheriff I've met out West here who cares what the law really is. Sure I'll teach you."

Tilghman's concern with the law mystified many a fellow sheriff, especially one in Texas he met a few months later. The case involved a man named George Snyder who stole a horse in Dodge and disappeared into "No Man's Land," the Panhandle area of Oklahoma which as yet had no government or legal status and was refuge for thieves and murderers. Since Tilghman knew every rock and river in the area he was sent to arrest Snyder. After a fruitless search he heard that Snyder was in Mobeetie, Texas, a town 350 miles south of Dodge.

First he went to Topeka to obtain an extradition request from the Governor, then to Kansas City and down the MKT railroad to Austin, where he presented the papers to the Governor of Texas. From there he took the train to Gainesville, then by stagecoach to Mobeetie.

He found Snyder in one of the saloons, watching a poker game. Standing on the balls of his feet, his hands at his side, he called, "Snyder, I'm a law officer. You're wanted in Dodge City. You're under arrest."

Snyder whirled around. "You can't arrest me in Texas!"

"The governor has signed your extradition, so come along quietly."

Snyder ducked under the table, crawled out the far side and headed toward the door. Tilghman dove after him, scattering cards and chips and players, caught Snyder by the ankle and brought him down. The man continued to scramble, so Tilghman hit him flush on the jaw and knocked him out.

The marshal of Mobeetie now entered the saloon and received from Tilghman the extradition papers signed by his governor. He read the paper carefully, looked down at

the unconscious man, then turned to Tilghman with a per-
plexed expression on his face.

"All this trouble over a horse thief? Whyn't ya jest shoot
him?"

As the cattle business boomed, so did Dodge City. The
time came when the civic leaders wanted more law enforcement than the Ford County sheriff's office could provide.
Mayor Bob Wright, owner of the town's largest general store,
led the move to draft Bill Tilghman out of the sheriff's office
and into the new job of City Marshal. Sheriff Pat Sughrue,
who had succeeded Masterson, objected violently to losing
his under-sheriff but he could not stand against the town.

In a public ceremony held in the mayor's store, Bill had
pinned on him the badge of his office, a badge like nothing
seen before or since. The town had taken up a collection of
money and given it to the jeweler to make the badge.
From a gold bar was suspended a $20 gold piece. On one
side was engraved *City Marshal;* on the other side were the
words *William Tilghman, from your many friends. Dodge
City, 1884.*

The town budget allowed Bill one deputy, and he appointed Tom Nixon, an old friend who operated a livery
stable in Dodge. Tilghman issued only one order to his
deputy:

"Tom, we gotta give Dodge a new reputation. I want it to
be known as the town you can't shoot up."

They divided the day between them, Tilghman giving
himself the most dangerous shift, three in the afternoon until
three in the morning. He unobtrusively entered every dance
hall and saloon and gambling parlor—the Alamo, the Lone
Star, the Lady Gay, Kelley's Place That Keeps Kelley. He
developed what could only be called extrasensory percep-
tion. By a casual stroll through town he could tell where
trouble was apt to break out later in the night. He could spot
the sullen, withdrawn look that often masked a need for
violence; he caught the furtive and scheming expression

that marked a man on the make. Whenever trouble occurred Tilghman was almost certain to be present and to damp it out quickly.

"I'd like the town council to pass a new law," Tilghman said to Mayor Wright one day. "I'd like a law that says no one but law officers can carry a gun inside the city limits."

"Bill, you're not serious, are you?" the mayor asked.

"Yes, sir. I am."

"But you could never enforce it. Wearing a gun is . . . well, a Western tradition."

"A bad tradition, it seems to me."

"I agree with you but . . ."

"You give me the law and I'll enforce it," Tilghman said confidently.

After the law was passed, Bill or his deputy met the incoming cowboys with a set little speech: "Boys, we got a new law here that says nobody can wear his gun in town limits. This law is to prevent you shooting somebody, but also to prevent somebody shooting you. You just give your guns to me now, and when you get ready to leave town you can pick them up at Wright's General Store. Now, if you're cheated by a crooked gambler, if anybody serves you watered whiskey, you just come and tell me and I'll take care of it. Welcome to Dodge City. Go have a good time and stay out of trouble."

After such a greeting few men objected to surrendering their guns, and a surprising number admitted they had never really wanted to carry them in the first place.

As Tilghman's reputation spread throughout the frontier there were men who scoffed and boasted they would "cut him down a few inches" next time they visited Dodge City. Late in the summer of 1884 two dusty and trail-stained strangers rode into town, hitched their horses to a rail and entered the nearest saloon. While pouring their drinks the bartender informed them that it was against the law to wear a gun in Dodge City.

Two men looked the bartender up and down, then one of them said, "Mister, what are you paid to do?"

"Why, to tend bar."

The stranger feigned great surprise. "You mean to tell me you ain't paid to give advice? You do it for nothing? You got so danged much smartness in ya that you can just spread it around free?"

The saloon had grown silent and watchful. The bartender flushed but said nothing. The two men picked up the bottle of whiskey and two glasses and sat down at a table against the wall. They finished off two drinks in workmanlike manner, then began to address the room.

"Where's the marshal? Where's that *big* man? If he's so brave why ain't he here to arrest us for wearin' guns?" There was no response. "Hear tell he's real fast on the draw. He's got a chance to prove it, right now, right here. Somebody go tell him that if he's tired of livin', we're ready to help him end it."

Word of the strangers' threat was carried to Tilghman's office by a rancher named Sampson. When Tilghman stood up from his desk, Sampson said, "Bill, I don't think you should go to that saloon. They're two of them and they're ugly drunk. You just might get yourself killed."

"Well, look at it this way," Tilghman said. "Suppose I didn't go. What then? Within twenty-four hours we'd have gunslingers ready to challenge me in every saloon in town."

When the marshal stepped through the saloon's swinging doors, the customers scrambled to get out of the line of fire. Tilghman saw the armed men and walked directly to their table. "Boys," he said, extending his two empty hands, "I'll have to take your guns. They're not allowed in town."

Whether or not the two men had actually begun to draw on Tilghman was a question debated in the saloon for the rest of that night. In any event, there were a number of customers who *thought* they were drawing and jumped them. The self-proclaimed bad men were carried to the floor under an avalanche of bodies. Their guns were removed and handed up to Tilghman.

The amazing thing was that a lawman had been assisted in a Dodge City saloon! The town was sure changing.

12

"I rode out to the ranch today," Bill said to Flora one evening after supper.

"Oh?" she said, continuing her crocheting. She was not fooled by his attempted casualness. Whenever he made big decisions he tried to make them appear small.

After a rather long silence Bill sighed heavily and said, "I guess you can't expect a hired hand to feel the same about the land as the man who owns it."

"The place in bad shape?"

"Well, no, but not in good shape, either." Bill allowed another thoughtful silence. "We ought to increase the herd. Beef's high and it's going higher. We got plenty of range to support more cattle. Couldn't expect the hired hand to run it properly, though."

She knew what was coming, had known for almost a month now. His silent restlessness had spoken as clearly to her as any words. She played the game—she asked what she was expected to ask: "What about your marshal's job, Bill?"

"I been on the job almost two years and Dodge has become a peaceable town. Tom Nixon can handle things."

"When do you want to move back?"

"Soon as you can conveniently get the family ready."

The family consisted of nine-year-old Charles (Flora's son by her first marriage and adopted by Tilghman) and seven-year-old Dorothy. Their first son, James, had died in infancy. Flora was pregnant with another son to be named William, Jr.

That September of 1886 the Tilghman family left Dodge and returned to the ranch. Again it was sunup to sundown labor, but the herd increased and the harvest from the vegetable garden was bountiful. Flora dared let herself think that at last they were sinking roots that would hold them to one place.

Tilghman's old friends and associates in Dodge were frequent visitors at the ranch, and late that fall Mayor Wright stopped by with some bad news. The Santa Fe railroad was pushing its tracks on west into Colorado, making a new terminal that would be closer to Texas than to Dodge City. The Texas cattlemen had already announced their intention of driving their herds to the new terminal.

After Wright had gone, Flora turned anxiously to her husband and asked, "What does it all mean?"

"The way I see it," he said, "there's no reason for Dodge City to exist except as a shipping point for cattle. Looks to me like she'll just shrink away."

"What does that mean to *us*, William?"

He gave her a reassuring smile. "Nothing. We've got the ranch. There's where a man's security lies, in the land."

Tilghman was both right and wrong. He was right about Dodge City; her reign as the lusty, rollicking queen of the cowtowns was nearing an end. He was wrong in believing his ranch was his security, for nature stepped in to alter the balance of things.

That winter the "great blizzard" came down from Manitoba, Canada, to seize the plains in iron grip. No one could remember such a cold and unrelenting storm. Each homesteading family sat huddled by the kitchen stove and listened to the bawling cattle as they slowly froze to death.

However cruel the storm, it had a sort of beauty. It took

gentle spring to melt the snows and reveal the horror beneath—the dead and decomposing cattle which dotted the
plains. Each farmer reacted to the disaster according to
his temperament. Some secretly wept, some got drunk, some
were blasphemous, some immediately surrendered.

A few were like Tilghman—stubborn.

Flora moved close beside him as they walked their fields
that spring to make the ghastly inventory. At last he said,
"We'll have to start over, rebuild the herd. There won't be
another winter like this one in our lifetime and the land is
still here, the good land."

As the sun warmed the earth Tilghman watched for the
first tender shoots of prairie grass. They did not appear on
schedule and he began to worry. With a spade he cut a
square of sod and lifted it to look at the roots. They were
brown and brittle and dead. The blizzard had destroyed
the range grass, and all Tilghman's stubbornness could not
restore its life. With no range grass there could be no cattle.
Some day nature would restore the range, but not in time
for the Tilghman family.

"We just gotta find other land," Tilghman said to Flora.
"I hear the government is opening up some of the Indian
Territory to homesteading this spring. I think I'd better go
down there and take a look."

The land Tilghman referred to was part of 70,000 square
miles bounded on the east by Arkansas, on the north by
Kansas, on the west by the 100th meridian, and on the
south by the Red River. These boundaries were eventually
to enclose the State of Oklahoma, but at the moment the
land was divided into two sections—the eastern half called
Indian Territory, the western half Oklahoma Territory.
Oklahoma Territory had been opened to homesteaders six
years earlier; the delay on opening the eastern half being
due to a "delicate situation." This "delicate situation" was
simply the fact that the government didn't really own the
land.

Back in 1820 the United States, in a brief seizure of con-

science, had given some of this land to the Five Civilized
Tribes, so-called because of the high order of their culture.
This grant was to compensate for their ancestral land hav-
ing been taken from them by the white man with shot and
sword. The Cherokees had been driven from North and
South Carolina, the Creeks from South Carolina and Ala-
bama, the Seminoles from Florida, the Chickasaw from
Georgia, and the Choctaw from Mississippi.

Now, sixty-nine years later, these tribes were to be once
more dispossessed. The government employed a euphemism,
announcing that only the tribes' "surplus land" would be
taken and paid for. There was, in fact, no such thing. The
tribes could barely sustain themselves on the land originally
given them, and now they were to be squeezed into smaller
and smaller reservations.

Prudently, the government did not let the white settlers
take all the "surplus land" at once. There would be a total
of six major land runs spread over eleven years. The Five
Civilized Tribes would be dispossessed in 1889; the Shawnee,
Potawatomi, Iowa, Sac and Fox in 1891; Cheyenne and
Arapaho in 1892; Tonkawa, Pawnee, and the Cherokee
Outlet in 1893; Kickapoo in 1895; Kiowa and Comanche (by
lottery) in 1901.

When Tilghman arrived at the Indian Territory's northern border for the first run, he came upon the camps of tens
of thousands of homesteaders, all waiting for that magic
moment—high noon, April 22, 1889. There were farm families with rude wagons containing the essentials for sur-
vival—a plow, an ax, and a gun. There were merchants,
their wagons piled high with calico and pans and soap.
There were whiskey traders and gamblers and accommodat-
ing ladies. There were lawyers and politicians, preachers
and carpenters, bankers and blacksmiths. There was everything needed to "civilize" the Indian land.

Many of these men were "Boomers," an organization put
together a number of years before by David Payne for the
frank purpose of pressuring Congress to open these lands to

white settlement. Their moment of triumph was at hand, and they established a string of camps for their members along the border. For a small fee the Boomers would help a man make out his claim under the new laws. These professional promoters dressed up their services with high moral purpose, and no public meeting ended without recourse to the Bible. David Payne's favorite posture was to stand with feet spread, his arm flung heavenward, his voice proclaiming in organ tones, "And the Lord commanded unto Moses, 'Go forth and possess the Promised Land.'"

He ignored the fact that the land had been promised before.

When Tilghman arrived he found he was no stranger. There were buffalo hunters he had known on the plains, cowboys with whom he had made drives, here and there a gunslinger he had escorted out of Dodge City, and a number of farmers and ranchers who had been ruined by the blizzard, just as he had been. One of the first things he saw was a covered wagon that had inscribed on the canvas top, IN GOD WE TRUSTED, IN KANSAS WE BUSTED. LET HER RIP, WE'RE BOUND FOR THE STRIP.

Each day saw new men arrive, until the total was near 100,000. It was clear there would not be enough land for all and tempers grew short. Fist fights were frequent and every man thought his neighbor a potential "Sooner." Sooners were men who sneaked over the border days or weeks before the starting hour, planning to hide themselves until the run started and then appear and lay claim to the choice lands. The United States Cavalry had swept through the Territory, flushing out the Sooners and sending them back across the border, where their lives were in jeopardy. There was much talk of lynching, though none actually occurred.

The night before the run Tilghman conferred with a half dozen old friends from Kansas. "This will be a bad night," he said, "and I think we should camp together and mount a watch. We've all got blooded horses, as fast as any in the Territory. Several times today I've caught men eying my horse. There's going to be a lot of horse stealing tonight. Let's not let it happen to ours."

Horses were indeed stolen that night, but none from Tilghman's camp.

As the next morning wore on, something just short of hysteria gripped the people. Men fought and cursed to get next to the starting line. If it hadn't been for the soldiers who guarded the border, the run would have begun at once. The Atchison, Topeka & Santa Fe Railroad had tracks through the Territory and scheduled special trains for the homesteaders who had no other transportation. As the train nosed to the starting line, a wave of humanity swept over it, seeming to submerge it. Men and women filled the coaches, the platforms between, climbed to the roofs, clung to the cowcatcher, filled the coal tender, even tried to invade the cab until the engineer and fireman drove them out with shovels.

At 11:30 the brawling became louder, the battles for position on the starting line more desperate. Tilghman and his friends did not join in; with swift horses under them they could afford to start from the third or fourth row. They were headed for the proposed new town of Guthrie where Tilghman planned to construct a commercial building and use the rent from it to stock a ranch.

At 11:45 an uneasy hush began to settle all along the line. Men were husbanding their strength for the dash, just fifteen minutes away. At 11:55 a booted U. S. Cavalry trooper rode slowly to a high point of ground. He carried a bugle, a flag and a watch. The thin line of soldiers, extending to the east and to the west as far as could be seen, held their rifles pointed skyward. Silence enveloped the land, a total silence that was as eerie as the babble had been minutes before. All eyes were on the bugler who held his large pocket watch before his face. The final minute seemed an eternity.

The two hands of the watch merged. It was twelve o'clock noon! The trooper put the bugle to his lips and blew a single piercing note, at the same moment waving the flag. At this signal, the cavalrymen discharged their rifles into the air. The gunfire was not heard, it was smothered beneath a human roar as thousands plunged over the starting line, wave upon wave, a human flood. Horses reared and cried out from the pain of whip and spur applied by men with contorted faces. They galloped in a great cloud of dust, looking like a rapacious army driven to some hellish destiny.

Whenever a wagon broke down the family would pour out of it to drive a stake into the ground, marking their claim. The train engines poured black smoke from their tall stacks and shrieks came from the whistles. At first the passengers laughed and sang and waved hats and handkerchiefs, but as horsemen began to outstrip the train, they turned on the engineer with angry cries and curses. Men began to throw themselves from the train and where they fell, that was their claim.

Tilghman and his friends were soon in the lead and they searched the horizon for the spot that was to become Guthrie. In mid-afternoon they came upon it, a tall pole with an American flag nailed to the top. They reined their horses, studied the land for a moment, then drove their claim stakes into the ground. By nightfall every homestead and town lot had been staked. Guthrie (as well as Oklahoma City to the south) had grown to 10,000 souls.

Guthrie was a city of tents. Several men decided to form a bank and did so by simply printing the fact on a piece of canvas and hanging it over the tent entrance. Lawyers painted their names and occupation on the sides of their tents. Saloons served their beverages from planks resting on boxes. Bordello tents found it unnecessary to advertise their services, their customers seemed to have a highly developed sense of direction.

Land speculation flourished through the night. Some men had staked claims only in order to sell them. There were claim jumpers, men who waited for the rightful owner to leave his land on some errand, then moved in to occupy it.

Sooners were sought out and denounced. One man who was among the first to arrive and stake a valuable claim, rode a horse lathered with white flecks of sweat and saliva—proof of his hard ride down from the border. When a suspicious citizen examined the lather, tasted it, it proved to be soap. The Sooner was driven from town at gunpoint.

Through all this, prayer and revival meetings were being held in a variety of tent tabernacles. The Boomers had called this the "Promised Land," and it was time for thanksgiving.

On that first night men tended to conduct their lives as they always had, but with increased fervor; the prayers were more emotional, the drunken brawls more violent, the land deals sharper, hopes for the future soared higher. And on the following morning the hangover, both physical and spiritual, was monumental—for Guthrie was now in chaos. No fresh water was available, no garbage disposal organized, no latrines dug, no law enforcement visible, no fire protection even thought of. Compounding these problems was the fact that there were no streets. The town was a solid mass of tents, and to travel so much as a mile was an exhausting process of weaving around tents, tripping over ropes, bumping into barrels, stepping on people.

While the Federal Government had designated the town site, it had not bothered to survey the land nor lay out a street plan. The first arrivals had staked out a few streets, but the waves of men that followed ignored the markings and made their claims where they wanted to. Some order had to be brought to Guthrie, or there would be not only disease, but terror, the rule of the gun.

A "Committee of 50" was organized to select town officials and draw up ordinances. They chose D. B. Dyer as mayor, and one of his first acts was to summon Bill Tilghman.

"Tilghman," the mayor said, "we got some big problems on our hands and there's a lot of Kansas men around here who say you're the one who can solve 'em."

"Kansas men have been known to exaggerate a bit," Bill grinned.

There were some good-natured guffaws among the committee members standing around, and then the mayor listed the problems. When he had finished, Bill said, "As I see it, Mr. Mayor, the first thing to do is clear some streets."

"Agreed. Will you do it?"

"I'll do it. But I'll need some equipment."

"Everything you want."

"I'll need a deputy, who I'll choose myself. You supply me with two teams of mules, two long logs, and some heavy chain."

The mayor looked puzzled, but he nodded his head without asking for an explanation.

"Also, Mr. Mayor, I'd like you to issue a proclamation that Oklahoma Avenue must be cleared by noon two days hence. We can take care of the side streets afterwards."

The mayor composed his proclamation and throughout the day it was read up and down the area designated as Oklahoma Avenue. Each reading brought forth cries of pain and anger. Though the proposed street had been marked, many men had staked claims in the middle of it without seeing the poles, and they now felt they were being victimized. Moreover, there were hard-core gamblers and saloonkeepers and gunmen who had laid claim to what seemed sure to be the most valuable business lots in town and they had no intention of giving them up.

That evening Tilghman and his deputy, Jim Masterson, Bat's brother, discussed strategy. "How far we gonna go on this?" Jim asked. "I mean, if a man refuses to move off, we gonna gun him?"

"If a man refuses to move, we move him."

"What if he draws on us?"

"I've seen a lot of men draw without having the guts to shoot."

"But what if he does shoot?" Masterson persisted.

"Then *we* shoot."

Jim grinned. "I just wanted to know where we stand."

"Where we stand is simple and clear. We're the law and we gotta win. Whatever it takes, we gotta win. If we don't clear that street, this won't be a town, it'll be an inferno."

Next morning the town seethed with rumors and counter-rumors. The mayor had fired Tilghman. Tilghman had fired the mayor. Vigilantes would clear the street. Vigilantes would gun down Tilghman. The United States Cavalry would be called in. The President of the United States had canceled all claims and the land was to be returned to the redskins.

As the noon deadline approached, hundreds gravitated to the designated street to watch. There was a Roman carnival atmosphere; the citizens had come to be entertained, to witness a test of strength, perhaps even bloodshed. The majority understood the necessity of streets and supported what action was necessary to create them. But at the same time they lived in the frontier tradition of independence and defiance of authority, and their admiration went to the men who refused to be pushed around. With their self-interest at war with their emotions, they would end up cheering the side that won. Tilghman understood this. He had to win today, there might not be another chance.

At exactly noon there was a stir in the crowd as a strange parade moved into position at the head of the street. First came Tilghman, his large-brimmed Western hat straight on his head, his handlebar mustache carefully combed, his face calm. Tilghman was always impressive on horseback, he rode with ease and dignity. Behind him came two drovers, each leading a team of mules attached by Jim Masterson who rode with arrogance. And behind him chains to long, heavy logs. The two logs, end to end, marked the width of the street, and when dragged through town would level all tents in their path.

Tilghman reined his horse and held up his hand for silence. He read the mayor's proclamation aloud, then added, "I will now clear the street. I have sent a man

ahead to warn the people to get out of the way. If any
man doesn't move, I will have to move him." He turned to
the drovers and said in a lower voice, "Take it slow, give
them plenty of time to get out of your way, but don't stop."

"*Haweee!*" the drovers shouted to the mules. "*Haweee!*"

The logs began to move and men scurried to strike their
tents and get them to safety. The street cleared and opened,
foot by foot. Then there was a blockage. A man stood spread-
legged in the middle of the street, a gun in his hand, his
face red from whiskey and sun and rage. "You ain't takin'
my claim," he screamed. "Do you hear me, you sonofabitch?
You're nothin' but a claim jumper, Tilghman, and I'm gonna
treat you like every skunk claim jumper should be treated."

Tilghman slid from his horse and began to walk slowly
toward the enraged man. The crowd was silent with antic-
ipation. This was what they had come for. As Tilghman
neared him the man screamed curses in an unending stream.
Tilghman had loosened his gun in its holster but did not
draw it. They were a yard apart when Tilghman stopped
and stared fixedly into the man's eyes. Then he made his
move, and it was so lightning fast that many of the spectators were not sure what happened. With his left hand Tilghman knocked the man's gun hand straight up into the air,
and with his right fist struck him on the point of his chin.
Soundlessly, the man crumpled to the ground and lay still.

Tilghman turned to the spectators and said matter-of-
factly, "Carry him out of the road."

A cheer went up. The crowd now knew who its favorite
was. Within an hour's time the whole length of Oklahoma
Avenue was cleared.

Order and prosperity came to Guthrie and toward the
end of the year Washington designated it the territorial
capitol. The grateful town would have given Tilghman any
high office he wanted but pressing personal problems would
not let him accept.

As was his original plan, Tilghman built a commercial
structure on his Oklahoma Avenue lot, and the rent from it

was put aside to re-establish himself as a rancher. By the time of the next land run on September 22, 1891 (opening the Shawnee, Potawatomi, Iowa, Sac and Fox lands) Tilghman was ready. He staked his claim on the banks of Bell Cow Creek, just outside the designated new town of Chandler. In opening this land Washington had accorded Civil War veterans "preference rights," which meant they could claim a homestead without actually making the run. Under this ruling Tilghman made a claim for his father a few miles southeast of Chandler. Then he went back to Dodge City to collect his family—wife, children, father, mother, nieces—and bring them to their new homes.

After delivering his parents and nieces to their land, Tilghman turned his team and wagon toward his own. In the back of the wagon, wedged in among the household goods, were his children, Bill, Jr., Dorothy, and baby Vonia. His stepson Charles was grown and working for the Wells Fargo Express Company in Guthrie. On the seat beside him was Flora, her hands clenched in mounting excitement.

"You did say we have a house?" she asked.

He laughed. "I've said it near six times since leaving Dodge. Do you think I'd put you in a tent?"

"I've lived in them," she said with a touch of pride. What she wanted to ask, but didn't, was if their home was a sod house.

Much of the Oklahoma prairie was black gumbo inter-laced with grass roots. It held strongly together and could be cut by a spade into square blocks and laid up in a wall like bricks. Such houses tended to leak dirt in the dry seasons and mud in the wet, insects and worms shared occupancy with the people, but there was one great advantage—the building material was free.

Tilghman knew the question in his wife's mind but he refused to help her say it; he wanted to surprise her.

Thirty minutes later the team labored up a hill and at the crest was pulled to a halt. "There it is," Tilghman said with a sweep of his hand. Below, next to a stream, was their house. There was timber on his claim, and Tilghman had constructed a log house of two stories and six rooms. Such size and privacy was all but unheard of in the frontier country.

"Oh, Bill!" Flora said. Then she covered her face with her hands and wept.

The Tilghman land was to blossom beyond anything seen in the area. Bill put in an orchard of peach trees that bore delicious fruit. He sent to Iowa for seed corn and his crop was so superior that neighbors begged for some of the seed. He kept milch cows and raised a pure strain of hogs. He was the first man in the territory to raise alfalfa. He bred and fought game chickens. Horses were his principal interest and with Neal Brown, his one-time hired hand back in Kansas, he set up a breeding farm. He loved to race his horses and entered meets as far away as St. Louis.

As his farm prospered and his influence grew, Tilghman seemed well on his way to becoming landed gentry. But it was not to be. For all of his love of the land, he could not forever tend it. There was the old restlessness in him. Flora knew this, but she was not a woman who tried to change a man. She concentrated on being thankful for those tranquil days allotted her.

13

On March 4, 1893, Grover Cleveland was inaugurated to his second term as President of the United States and was immediately importuned by a delegation of political and business leaders from the Territory of Oklahoma. The Indians had been pretty well "pacified," they told the President, but now their property and lives were being threatened by white men turned outlaw.

Horse thieves, cattle rustlers, hold-up men and plain gunfighters were making life so hazardous that some settlers were talking of giving up their homesteads and returning East. Oklahoma was a rich and beautiful land, but if law and order were not soon imposed, it could revert to a wilderness.

Perhaps there was some exaggeration in these words spoken to the President, but not much. Between 1890 and 1900 there were 250 Western train robberies, and in that same period sixty-five lawmen were killed. No count had been kept of saloons held up, of cattle rustled, of horses stolen, but the number was great.

The very terrain favored the outlaws. A man could disappear in the vastness of the plains, or he could hide out in the mountains and caves to the west. Coming out of Texas and running north and west through Oklahoma Territory was "Horse Thief Trail," and in this sparsely settled area many homesteaders fed and sheltered the outlaws. Some of these farmers and ranchers were Sooners, some had married squaws to get Indian land, others had had their own trouble with the law back East and come here to be anonymous. For one reason or another, their sympathies or their self-interest lay with the thieves. But even the law-abiding rancher found himself feeding and sheltering any outlaws who came his way. It was either that or have his own cattle rustled, his own small savings taken from him at gunpoint.

The problem was of such dimension, the Oklahomans told President Cleveland, that only the Federal Government could cope with it. The President agreed, and two months later he appointed Evett Nix as United States Marshal for the Oklahoma Territory and instructed him to appoint enough Deputy U. S. Marshals to impose law on the land.

The selection of Nix raised a few eyebrows. He was not the blood-and-guts sort of man the territory had hoped for. He was a thirty-two-year-old Guthrie merchant, a partner in the firm of Baldwin & Nix, general merchandise, and the firm of Nix & Halsell, wholesale grocers. He was unassuming, immaculately groomed, his hair parted sedately in the middle, his mustache trimmed, his linen changed daily. He was highly regarded by all who knew him, but was he the man for the job?

These misgivings were largely unspoken until the new marshal gave an interview to a reporter from the newspaper, *State Capitol*. Nix was quoted as saying: "No man who drinks can have a place on my staff. They will, above all, be courteous, of unimpeachable character and good standing in their communities . . . The time has gone by for swash-bucklers, for men who fence themselves with revolvers and cartridges. The revolver, with the men I appoint, will be for business, not for show. Men shall be treated as innocent, when arrested, until the law and evidence shall prove them guilty . . ."

The *State Capitol* commented editorially: "This means that none but the YMCA need apply . . . Think of a gentleman moralist, running into a tough . . . and in a plaintive voice declaring: 'My deah suh, we have been sent for you, suh, and we would like you to hold up youh hands and be ouh prisoner; if you don't, suh, as much as we dislike to, we will be compelled, suh, to pull ouh guns on you.'"

Nix was stung by the editorial but had no intention of modifying his standards. He did, however, seek expert advice. One of the first men he sought out was Bill Tilghman.

"Bill," he said after they had seated themselves in the back of his general store, "how do you see the problem?"

Tilghman replied, "First off, we gotta realize that it was bound to come."

Nix looked surprised. "You mean to say that no matter what we did in the past, we'd still have these outlaws shooting up the territory?"

"Something like that. With a few exceptions, most of our bad men are ex-cowboys, unemployed cowboys. When the homesteaders moved in to claim the land and fence it off, the open range was gone, the great herds were gone, and so were the jobs for cowboys."

"They could have homesteaded like everyone else."

"A man who could settle down and feed chickens is not the kind of man who would be a cowboy in the first place. When the plains were open range, we needed wild men for a wild job. Now the jobs are gone, but we can't expect the men to change. They figure they got a gripe, that they've been double-crossed."

"How double-crossed?" Nix demanded.

"Last week I had a rancher say to me, 'God made this cow country, why else would it be so big and have such good grass? Washington can't change God's plan, can't cut it up into measly little gardens. And any time I see a man stringin' a fence, I aim to give him some lead poisoning.'"

"I've heard that sort of talk," Nix agreed. "What'd you say to him?"

"I said it appeared to me that God might have originally intended the land for the buffalo. I said the cowmen had taken the land from the Indians, just as the farmers were now taking it from the cowmen. I wasn't quite certain where God stood in all these transactions."

"Damn it, Tilghman, it's gone beyond a range war. A lot of these men have become gunfighters, they hold up trains and banks, they kill people. You seem to be defending them."

"Not at all," Tilghman said calmly. "But when a marshal rides out to arrest a man, it's well that he knows what sort of man he's after."

"I suppose you're right," Nix said slowly. "Bill, I've received a lot of ragging on my statement to the press about the kind of men I want as deputies. Am I wrong? Am I being too much YMCA in my approach? Are there such men around who will work for their government in this war?"

"I think you'll find them," Tilghman said judiciously.

"Be frank with me, Bill. If you were in my seat what else would you look for in a deputy?"

"Well, one important thing, I'd want to know how he handles his gun."

"Quick on the draw?"

"That, of course, but I'd also want him to be reluctant on the draw. The man who draws first is usually flustered and scared, and therefore inaccurate. He may get off the first shot but it usually misses and he sets himself up for deadly counterfire. A man who prides himself on shooting from the hip is a braggart, and a poor shot, to boot. I've known outlaws so obsessed with shooting first that they fired from an open-end swivel holster. I never saw a man even wounded by such a contraption. Some outlaws practice 'fanning' for hours every day. To use such methods in a real gunfight is to build yourself a coffin. No man is really accurate while riding a galloping horse. No man can be accurate shooting two guns at once.

"I'd want a deputy to know these things—from experience. I'd want him to be patient, to draw a gun only when he intended to use it. Oh, and I'd want him to use a Colt .45.

If you shoot a man with a lighter gun you may fatally wound him, but he may kill you before he dies. Shoot him with a .45 and he goes down at once, and stays down."

Nix had listened with great interest. Now he grinned and said, "Looks like I've got the right man. You'll take the job?"

"No job's been offered to me."

"I'm ready to swear you in as Deputy United States Marshal for the Oklahoma Territory."

"I'm ready to be sworn," Tilghman said.

On Tilghman's advice, Nix added Heck Thomas to the growing roster of Federal Marshals. Thomas was a solidly built six-footer with black hair always carefully combed. He was well coordinated and moved with grace. He had a horse named Limber Jim who could singlefoot beautifully, and when master and animal moved down the street the ladies sighed.

It was not for these qualities that Tilghman wanted him for a partner, but because he was a man who faced danger with an icy calm. Before coming to join Nix's force, he had been a Federal Marshal in the Fort Smith area of Indian Territory where he served out of Judge Isaac Parker's court. Parker ("The Hanging Judge") sentenced 160 men to death, hanged seventy-nine of them.

Following Nix's announcement of his appointment, the Kansas City *Times* wrote of Tilghman and Thomas: "These are wonderful men, and their appointment had a wonderful effect. The most notorious characters in town skipped out at the first intimation that they were not wanted. Others are going."

The Deputy U. S. Marshal job paid no salary, only fees. Each man received six cents a mile while on official business, out of which he paid transportation, board and room, and all other expenses. When he made an arrest he received $2. He could chase a desperado for weeks, still the fee was $2 if he caught him, nothing if he didn't. If sent to subpoena witnesses he received six cents a mile one way, fifty cents for the first witness served, thirty-five cents for each additional one. All in all, a Federal Marshal was lucky to make $500 for a year's dangerous work.

Under these conditions it was perhaps surprising that Nix was able to put together a staff of fifty seasoned men. There was a variety of motivations, of course. Some, such as Tilghman, had an independent income from land holdings; some wished adventure; some were ambitious; some enjoyed power. One thing they all shared was an aversion to confinement and routine. They were happiest when on a horse, riding through the sweet grass that ran to the horizon.

Of all the deputy marshals, Bill Tilghman was the best known and to him went the most difficult assignments. His first one was to establish law and order in Perry.

Perry was, at the moment, a vacant bit of prairie thirty miles north of Guthrie and in the middle of the Cherokee Outlet. This land was to be opened to white settlement with a run on September 16, 1893, at which time Perry would become (like Guthrie and Chandler and Oklahoma City before it) an instant town. A few lessons had been learned, however, and this time the streets were to be surveyed and clearly staked before the homesteaders came galloping up. "Government Square" was marked out and two wooden buildings constructed on opposite sides of it, one the Post Office and the other the Land Office. It was to the latter building that all men would come to file their homestead claims. It was here that passions would run highest, violence be most frequent. Bill Tilghman was put in charge of the Land Office.

The run followed the pattern of the previous ones. The starting gun was fired at twelve noon; by one o'clock the men on the fastest horses had arrived; by nightfall 10,000 people were camped in the new town. It was a night of drunken celebration for those who had successfully staked claims, for drunken quarrels among those who had not. At dawn the next morning the line began to form outside the

Land Office. Here, if a man could authenticate his claim, and if it was not disputed by another man (which frequently happened), he would receive a temporary deed good for five years. At the end of that time, if he had occupied or improved the land, his title became permanent.

Nerves were ragged that morning, not only with hangovers, but uncertainty. No man knew but that his claim was being jumped while he stood here in line. And the line, a thousand long, moved with excruciating slowness. The sun baked them, dust coated them, and the man who stepped out of line for any bodily need lost his place forever.

Tilghman had installed a clerical staff in the office, his job was outside. As he began to walk slowly down the line he saw a bull-necked man shove a little fellow out of line and take his place.

Tilghman stepped quickly up to the man and ordered, "Take your place at the end of the line."

The man turned bloodshot eyes on Tilghman, measuring him. He observed the carefully tailored clothing, the vest with lapels, the brocaded necktie casually but carefully formed into a large knot, the white ten-gallon hat whose crown was high and uncreased, the boots that actually seemed to be polished! The man made a conclusion. He snarled:

"That other feller stepped outta line, and I got a right to take his place. What you got to say to that, mister?"

Tilghman's hand shot out to gather his coat in a ball right beneath his chin. He jerked him out of line, grabbing the man's wrist as he did so and pulling his arm up behind his back in a hammer lock. Then he marched him down the long line, making him dance a bit with the pain in his shoulder. At the end of the line he released the arm and shoved the man into place.

A murmur of approval and gratitude ran down the line. "That's Bill Tilghman," men said to each other. "Won't be any trouble with him around."

There was no trouble in the Land Office, but there was

plenty in the rest of town, especially at night. Making his early rounds that evening, Tilghman heard angry voices coming from one of the tents. As he turned toward the tent a young man backed out of it, followed by a hand that held a gun pointed at his stomach. Tilghman stepped quickly beside the tent, jerked open the flap and pointed his own gun at the man inside. "Come out with your hands up," he commanded.

As the man stepped out Tilghman said, "Oh, it's Tenspot." Tilghman holstered his gun, as did the gambler. Turning to the young man, Tilghman said, "How much did he get from you, son?"

"Sixty dollars. I ain't got a cent left."

"He gambled it, fair and square," Tenspot whined.

"Fair and square!" Tilghman repeated with heavy irony. "You don't know what those words mean." He held out his hand. "Give me your roll." Tenspot stared at the ground without moving. Tilghman repeated the order, this time in a voice soft with menace. "Give me your roll, please."

The roll was a big one, and from it Tilghman peeled off $60 for the young man. The rest he tossed back to the gambler, saying, "I don't want sharpers in town."

"You can't prove nothin' on me," Tenspot boasted, but his eyes were anxious.

"By the way, they got a warrant out for you in San Antonio," Tilghman said, bluffing. "I might just send them a wire."

Tenspot became abject. "I won't cause no more trouble. I'll stay out of sight. I'll get out of town, anything you say. Give me a chance."

Turning his back, Tilghman took the boy by the arm and walked away. "You been drinking, son?" he asked.

"Yes, sir," sheepishly.

"Liquor makes some men feel twice as tough and twice as smart as everybody else. But there's always somebody around to take 'em down, usually somebody who hasn't been drinking. How old are you, son?"

1. Flora Kendall Tilghman, Tilghman's romantic first love, was embittered by the demands of his profession.

2. Zoe Stratton Tilghman, Tilghman's mettlesome second wife, could write poetry as well as she roped calves.

3. The start of the famous run of homesteaders into the Cherokee Strip, Indian Territory, in 1893.

4. This bleak half-dugout was typical of the primitive dwellings of early settlers in Oklahoma.

On Oklahoma Soddy
Copyrighted by Kedrick
No. 5.

5. The sod house was the homesteader's solution to the problem of building material on Oklahoma's treeless plains.

6. Company H, 13th Infantry, U.S. troops stationed on Cottonwood Creek near Guthrie in Indian Territory in 1889.

Co. H. 13th Inf.

7. The Merchant's Bank, first bank in Guthrie, was organized overnight by self-constituted bankers.

8. A mob around the Guthrie jail in 1889. Pioneer tempers were short and justice was apt to be swift.

"Eighteen."

"Maybe, sixteen?" Tilghman said gently.

"Well, yes, sir."

"This is a new town, a new country and there's going to be plenty of jobs, if you want to work. If, instead, you want to gamble, you'll find plenty of gamblers, too. You just gotta make up your mind which kind of life you want to live."

"I've learned my lesson, sir, really I have. I'll look for a job tomorrow."

"Come around to the Land Office. Maybe I can help you."

The boy presented himself the next morning and Tilghman got him a job clerking for a dry goods merchant. Tilghman's trust was properly placed, for the boy went on to become one of Oklahoma's prominent merchants and civic leaders. For the rest of his life he kept a picture of Bill Tilghman on the wall behind his desk.

"It's there to remind me," he explained to whomever asked, "that I owe a debt to that man. It's a debt I can only pay off by being tolerant and helpful to some other young man at a crossroad in his life."

Tilghman's conduct in Perry was not always so tolerant. Sometimes he had to rule by gun, especially in the area of Perry known as "Hell's Half Acre." It was considerably larger than a half acre, for it contained seventy saloons, along with gambling houses and dance halls. In this area men surrounded themselves with bales of hay when they lay down in their tents to sleep, thus creating a shield to absorb stray bullets.

One afternoon Tilghman took his old friend Fred Sutton on a tour through Hell's Half Acre. Fred had been buffalo hunting with Tilghman in the days of Dodge, and had staked claim to land both in Guthrie and Perry. While they reminisced about Dodge, Tilghman kept his eyes searching. Suddenly he touched Sutton on the arm, a signal to be alert.

"Hello, Sam," Tilghman called out to a lumpish man a few yards away. "When are you leaving town?"

"I'm leavin' when I'm damn good and ready," the man

snarled. On his forehead there was an ugly crescent-shaped scar which gave him the nickname of "Crescent Sam."

"Well, you better get good and ready by tonight," Tilghman said. "I don't want to see you in Perry after dark."

As they walked away, Tilghman said to Sutton, "That's Crescent Sam. He's a thief and a murderer. Wherever he is there's trouble."

"Maybe you've set him gunning for you, Bill," Sutton said.

"Maybe, but I don't think so. The thing is not to push a man like him too hard. Mean what you say, but give him some elbow room. If I'd told him to get out of town right this minute, he'd have probably gone for his gun. But I've given him several hours to think things over, and the odds are that he'll leave quietly."

Odds notwithstanding, Tilghman was wrong.

The Buckhorn was the town's biggest saloon. It operated in a circus tent, and six large kerosene lamps hung from the ridgepole to fill the place with a flickering golden light. On one side of the tent was the bar, opposite were the gambling tables, and at the far end a banjo orchestra which dispensed rhythmic, nasal music.

At about nine o'clock that night a howl suddenly filled the air in the Buckhorn. It rose high and quaveringly, sounding half human and half animal, and it came from Crescent Sam. Every man turned toward the strange cry, and even the banjos faltered and were silent.

At the end of his howl, Crescent Sam cried out, "I'm a she-wolf from Bitter Creek."

He pulled his gun and looked about belligerently. Many men avoided his half-mad eyes. He raised the gun at arm's length above his head and put two shots through the tent. "I'm ready," he cried. "Any man here who thinks he can throw me out of town? I'm waitin'."

The customers began to leave the bar and the gambling tables, flattening themselves against the tent walls or slipping outside. As the crowd melted away it left one man standing clear, Marshal Tilghman. As Crescent Sam saw him, he leveled his gun and fired. There were two shots close together and Crescent Sam took a bullet in his chest. He crumpled to the dirt floor, dead.

Tilghman holstered his gun, then said to a bartender, "Help me carry him outside."

When the body was removed, the drinkers and gamblers and musicians resumed their former activity, but with more gaiety. It had been a lively diversion.

14

Perry became incorporated and changed rapidly from a tent town to a wooden town.

The newly elected town council, headed by Mayor John Brogan, had many problems, but topping the list was law enforcement. The Federal Marshals had no local authority (except for Federal crimes) once a town became incorporated. Also, there was town pride involved; it demanded independence from the Federal Government, it wanted to run its own show. The trouble with Perry was that it wanted independence and Bill Tilghman, too.

During their first meeting, one councilman after another got up to praise him. One man said, "I never saw him rattled, I never heard him raise his voice, never saw him draw his gun in anger, and by God, I never saw him draw his gun without *winning!*"

Mayor Brogan said, "I take it we're all in agreement that Bill Tilghman would make the best city marshal we could find. But I'm not sure he'd give up his Federal job to come with us."

"Ask him . . . ask him!" the councilmen shouted.

"I will," Brogan said.

Brogan took the proposition to the Land Office where the

Federals—now numbering four—still had their headquarters. Tilghman listened to the offer without comment. Brogan concluded by saying, "We're not asking you to stay permanently, if you don't want to, but long enough to train a force, build a jail, and get the courts operating. You'd be doin' us a big favor, Marshal, if you could see your way clear."

"How soon do you have to know?" Tilghman asked.

"Yesterday be too soon for you?" Brogan grinned.

"A mite," Tilghman agreed. "How about the end of the week?"

"The end of the week," Brogan said.

That afternoon Tilghman discussed the offer with Heck Thomas. Thomas pulled at his mustache and pondered and finally said, "I dunno what to say, Bill, except how *I'd* feel about it."

"And how is that, Heck?"

"It's a town job, full of routine paperwork. That's not for me. I like to get out in the country."

"I feel the same way. But on the other hand, I do have some friends here, men who have done me favors, and I feel I owe them this. After all, it will only be for a few months."

"There's that," Thomas agreed.

"Frankly, the main thing that makes me hesitate is that Nix might not take me back as a Federal if I quit now."

"Ho!" Thomas hooted. "You're the best marshal in the whole area and Nix wouldn't dare not take you back."

"I'm afraid that's friendship talking," Tilghman said.

"Yeah? Well, why don't you ask him?"

Tilghman nodded. "I think I'll ride over to Guthrie first thing in the morning."

When Nix heard Tilghman's problem, he agreed to release him for two months on one condition—that he not resign his Federal job at all but merely take a leave of absence.

Within the allotted time Tilghman had completed his work in Perry and returned to Guthrie to resume his Federal job. He found Nix worried. "Bill, we're having trouble."

"That's our job," Tilghman grinned.

"We're having trouble where we shouldn't have it—with the county and town police. They seem resentful of us and we're getting less and less cooperation from them."

"That's nothing new. There's always been a degree of jealousy between Federal and state and town authorities. Human nature, I guess."

"It's never been this bad," Nix insisted. "Just remember that from now on we're going to have to develop all our own evidence and not count on local help."

Tilghman, who had been both town and Federal officer, thought Nix exaggerated the problem. He soon learned this was not the case.

George Maydele and Eugene Kile owned a saloon in the town of Perkins, forty miles northeast of Guthrie, and when they failed to pay their annual whiskey license fee, Tilghman was given a warrant to bring them into Federal Court in Guthrie. Bill rode to Perkins, found the right saloon and presented his warrant.

The saloon owners seemed resigned, but Kile said, "You ain't planning on starting back for Guthrie tonight, are you, Marshal?"

"Morning's soon enough," Tilghman said.

"Well, sir, under the law I reckon you could put us in jail overnight."

"Correct."

"You ever seen our jail here in Perkins? Sure ain't a very appetizing sight. If we promise to meet you here tomorrow morning . . ."

Tilghman waved his hand generously. "I'll release you two men on your own recognizance until tomorrow morning."

The next day Tilghman appeared in the saloon to find Kile giving instructions to his bartender about what was to be done in his absence. He greeted the marshal cordially. "Good morning, Mr. Tilghman. I'm about ready to start, but Maydele got delayed a bit. He'll be along shortly."

It was a subterfuge that might have worked except for the presence of an early customer. He spoke up: "George Maydele ain't gonna be here any too damn soon. Town Marshal arrested him this morning."

"What for?" Tilghman snapped.

"Not payin' his license to sell booze. He's down at the Justice of the Peace court. That's what I heard, anyway."

For once Tilghman all but lost his temper, and it was with himself for not having foreseen this trick. The local justice had no jurisdiction over whiskey licensing, but they apparently intended to brazen it through. By pleading guilty and taking a light fine, Maydele hoped to escape the Federal Court on the grounds of double jeopardy, the law that provides a man cannot be tried twice for the same crime.

The trial was proceeding in a sedate and friendly manner. The Justice of the Peace was named Utter, the town marshal was A. N. Woldridge, the town attorney was named Tillery, the defendant was, of course, George Maydele. The atmosphere of bonhommie was suddenly shattered when the courtroom door was jerked violently open and Tilghman marched into the room.

He pointed a finger at Maydele and said, "That man is my prisoner, in Federal custody." He glared at Justice Utter who squirmed and said nothing.

The lawyer spoke up. "He's been duly arrested and is being tried before this court."

"You're conducting a farce," Tilghman retorted. "You can't arrest a Federal prisoner. Come on, Maydele."

"You're disturbing this trial," Woldridge cried.

"Order in the court," the justice shouted.

Tillery, his voice high and thin with excitement, began to quote the law.

"There's another law you better learn about," Tilghman snapped. "It's called conspiracy to evade the law."

Tilghman stepped forward to reach for Maydele, but the town marshal jumped between them. Tilghman drew his gun and Woldridge promptly retreated. Grabbing Maydele firmly by the arm, Tilghman marched him out of the court-room.

The local newspaper reported what happened next:

> Marshal Tilghman, pointing his weapon at Woldridge, left the room with his man, and marched him uptown. This action so rattled the court that great disorder prevailed, and it is said J. Tillery ran from the room following Tilghman, shrieking, "Gimme a gun! Someone gimme a gun!"

Several bystanders offered guns to Woldridge, but he somehow managed not to see them and returned to the court. Justice Utter thereupon issued a warrant for Tilghman's arrest, charging him with assault on Woldridge "with intent to kill." It was now Woldridge's duty to pursue Tilghman, serve the warrant and arrest him. But the town marshal discovered that he had more pressing business to attend to, and he assigned the job to Deputy Graham.

Graham found Tilghman in Maydele's and Kile's saloon, preparing to leave with his prisoners for Guthrie. Upon hearing the warrant read to him, Tilghman warned Maydele and Kile to wait for him while he returned to Justice Utter's court.

If Tilghman's first entrance had been explosive, this one was even more effective for its icy calm. He was well aware that he represented the dignity and the power of the Federal service, and he wasn't going to give an inch of it away.

The justice read the charge and then asked how Tilghman wished to plead, guilty or not guilty.

Tilghman said gravely, "I cannot plead at this time to such a serious charge. I ask for a continuance."

There was wrangling in the court, but Justice Utter dared not refuse. "I will hear this case Monday morning," he finally announced.

When Justice Utter gaveled his court open on Monday morning there was no sign of Tilghman; he was being represented by a United States District Attorney. Within minutes the Federal attorney had a legal hammerhold on Justice Utter and the case was reluctantly dismissed.

Back at the office in Guthrie, Tilghman was the object of good-natured kidding, but beneath the banter was concern over the deteriorating relationships with many towns.

15

A new pattern of crime now began to emerge on the plains. The era of the loner was ending, the outlaws began to run in gangs. Bank and train holdups were planned and executed with military precision. The town police found themselves largely unable to cope with the lightning strikes and quick withdrawals done under the protection of heavy fire power, and the war became more and more between the gangs and the Federal marshals.

In the late spring of 1893 Nix summoned Tilghman to his spare office and shut the door. He pointed wearily to a pile of letters on his desk. "Complaints. Complaints from Washington, D.C. *Official* complaints from Washington, D.C. They say that there's some outlaw gangs out here that haven't been put in jail."

"How'd they know?" Tilghman grinned.

"Last month, the holdup of the Santa Fe California Express at Cimarron . . ."

"Yes?"

"By some misfortune there were a couple of congressmen aboard that train that had their watches taken."

"We might take up a collection to buy them new ones," Tilghman grinned.

Nix was in no mood for quips. "Some say the Dalton gang did it."

Bill shook his head. "Not likely, after what happened to them at Coffeyville."

Back on October 5, 1892, the Dalton gang had attempted a double bank holdup in Coffeyville, Kansas. An aroused and armed citizenry battled them in the streets and killed Bob Dalton, the leader, Grat Dalton, Dick Boardwell and Bill Powers. Captured was Emmett Dalton; escaped was Bill Doolin. Doolin, in fact, didn't make the raid. His horse went providentially lame and he never kept the rendezvous.

"We know that the Dalton gang numbered more than the six men who rode into Coffeyville," Tilghman continued. "They may be still together but if so, they'll have a new leader and a new name."

"And . . . ?"

"My information indicates that the new leader is Bill Doolin."

"Let's stay on top of it," Nix said.

The next week there was a double holdup of trains in the Cherokee Outlet at Wharton. One train coming south was held at gunpoint by seven masked men until the north-bound train arrived, then both trains were plundered. Informers said that the outlaws were hiding in caves outside of Ingalls, Kansas. Ingalls had always been Dalton territory.

The citizens of Ingalls had made a decision: It was better business, and safer, to accept outlaws than to fight them. In return for not preying on the local merchants, an outlaw could get drunk in an Ingalls saloon without having to shoot his way out, and he could rent a bed in Mary Pierce's hotel (with or without a girl in it) and not have to worry about waking up with a sheriff's gun in his chest.

Acting on the information that the Wharton train robbers were in Ingalls, Deputy U. S. Marshal John Hixon rode into town with a posse that included Lafe Shadley, Tom Houston, Dick Speed and Jim Masterson. The outlaws were

there all right, and waiting for the posse. The moment
the Federal men arrived in front of Mary Pierce's hotel they
were caught in a vicious crossfire. The fight raged up and
down the main street, with men firing from behind every
pillar, water barrel and wagon. When the battle finally
ended, Lawmen Speed and Shadley lay dead in the street.
There was little to show for their deaths. An outlaw named
Arkansas Tom had been captured, but the rest of the gang
had escaped.

Tilghman was again called into Nix's office. "It looks
like Ingalls proves you right, Bill. It's the Doolin gang we
have to get. I'm relieving you from all assignments except
one—get Doolin! Washington has set up a special fund and
you can have all the money and men you need to do the
job."

"Better done with fewer men than many," Tilghman said,
"at least in the beginning."

"You name them."

"Heck Thomas."

"Right," Nix nodded.

"Chris Madsen."

"Madsen," Nix agreed.

"That's all for now. What's to be done must be done
quietly."

Tilghman had chosen as his principal aides two men
who were physically unlike. Where Thomas was groomed
and graceful, Madsen was short and round and rumpled,
and seemed to perch atop a horse with the precariousness
of a pumpkin. But appearances belied the man, for Madsen
was a true soldier of fortune. Born in Denmark, he served
a term in the Danish army, fought in the Franco-Prus-
sian War, joined the French Foreign Legion in Algiers,
come to America to hunt buffalo and be an Indian scout,
served a hitch in the U. S. Army as quartermaster sergeant
of the 5th Cavalry.

What Tilghman, Thomas and Madsen shared was a quiet

tenacity, a cool courage, and complete devotion to each other. They became known throughout the West as "The Three Guardsmen."

When the three of them conferred later that day, Tilghman said, "What do we really know about Doolin?"

"An ex-cowhand," Thomas said. "Suppose to have worked on the HX-Bar Ranch."

"What turned him bad? What are his weaknesses?" Tilghman asked. "Whom does he trust? Does he have any grudges? Any girl friends?"

None of them knew.

"It would seem to me," said Tilghman, "that the first thing for us to do is ride the frontier from Kansas to Texas, visit every ranch and farm, and see what we can find out about Doolin and his men. We can meet back here in Guthrie next month and compare notes."

Some days later Tilghman arrived at the HX-Bar Ranch. It was a large spread along the banks of the Cimarron River and owned by the wealthy Texas cattleman, Oscar Halsell.

"Yeah, Bill Doolin worked for me," Halsell replied to Tilghman's question. "He came up from Arkansas, a skinny, six-foot blond kid who couldn't read nor write, couldn't ride a proper horse and couldn't rope a lame cow."

"How was it you hired him?" Tilghman asked.

"He could use an ax, and none of my cowboys could do that. We were building corrals and Bill Doolin could split rails like nobody I'd ever seen." Halsell paused, smiled apologetically, and said, "I didn't hire him for that reason, either. I didn't know he could use an ax until after he was on the payroll."

"Why did you hire him, Mr. Halsell? I'm not being critical, you haven't broken any law, I'm just trying to understand what kind of a man Doolin is."

"Well, damn it, he was so young and eager to learn, and he could put on a big, shy smile that just made you want to give him a hand up. I figured him a kid with ambition, and I was right. He'd spend a long day chopping and splitting wood, and each evening pore over books, teaching himself to read and write. Then he badgered the cowboys until they taught him how to ride and rope and shoot. He turned out to be the best all-round hand I had."

"Did you fire him, Mr. Halsell?"

"No, sir. He quit."

"Why did he quit?"

Puzzled, "I dunno. I'd hire him back tomorrow, if he come askin'."

"You know he's turned outlaw?"

"I heard tell."

"Why do you suppose he did that, Mr. Halsell? He doesn't seem to fit into any pattern. Some cowboys turn outlaw when they lose their jobs, but that's not the case with Bill Doolin. As far as I can see, he hasn't been wronged, he has no grudges, nothing to avenge. How do you figure him?"

Halsell frowned at the ground, kicked a hole in the dirt with the pointed toe of his expensive boot. "I been givin' that some wonder," he finally said. "He ain't an outlaw because of meanness, nor even for the money. It's for excitement, near as I can figure. If the Indian wars was still hot he'd a been an Indian fighter. If he'd been born earlier he'd been a hero in the Civil War. But things is all quietin' down, gettin' peaceable, and Bill has got to stir up his own excitement. There's a wildness in him that makes him do it. You may not think this is much of an answer, Marshal, but it's all I got."

"It's as good an answer as I've found so far," Tilghman said, extending his hand to the rancher. "If you hear anything about Doolin or his gang, I'd appreciate knowing."

Tilghman turned to leave and had taken a half dozen steps when the rancher called after him.

"Just because Doolin ain't got hot blood in him don't

mean he ain't dangerous. As I see it, it's the cool ones who is most dangerous of all."

Tilghman nodded. "I thank you for your warning, sir."

Bit by bit Tilghman and his associates were able to piece together the gang's personnel. Doolin's chief assistant was Bill Dalton, a bitter and vindictive man. Bill, alone of all the Dalton brothers, had tried to go straight. He had been a member of the California State Legislature with ambition to become a senator when the Coffeyville events destroyed his career. Though he was miles away, and innocent of all knowledge, his political party dumped him on the theory that the voters believed "blood will tell." When he came to Coffeyville to visit his wounded and jailed brother Emmett, only quick action by the sheriff saved him from being lynched by the outraged citizens.

He left Coffeyville to find the gang, join it and avenge himself on a society that was persecuting him. Being a Dalton, he expected to inherit the leadership of the gang, but again he was frustrated. It was now the Doolin gang and the best position he could hope for was number two.

Besides Doolin and Dalton there were eight other members of the gang. "Little Bill" Raidler was the intellectual of the gang. He was a Dutchman from Pennsylvania where he had been well grounded in the classics. When drunk, he quoted Chaucer, to the great boredom of the rest of the gang. He had a specialty. He drilled a hole in each bullet, filled it with dynamite, then plugged it over with lead. When he shot a man, the bullet would enter the body, then explode inside of him.

George ("Red Buck") Weightman also had a specialty: he was a skilled horse thief. Having a good supply of fast horses was of primary concern to Doolin, and Red Buck always did the job quietly and fast.

George ("Bitter Creek") Newcomb had worked with Doolin on the Halsell ranch, as had Red Buck. He was movie-star handsome, but his face was moody. In the frontier it was considered poor manners, if not downright dangerous, to ask a man where he came from. A popular ballad of the day ran:

> What was your name in the States?
> Was it Thompson or Johnson or Bates?
> Did you murder your wife
> And flee for your life?
> What was your name in the States?

When asked where he came from, Newcomb always replied, "Bitter Creek," thus his nickname. His darkly brooding face and his tragic-sounding name made him quite irresistible to women.

Dick ("Little Dick") West was a waif. He grew up without a family and when he was a spindly and undersized child of sixteen, living out of garbage cans in Decatur, Texas, the foreman of the 3-Circle Ranch hired him for odd jobs. He learned to ride and became a cowboy, finally leaving the 3-Circle to work for Halsell on the HX-Bar Ranch. There he met Doolin, Red Buck and Bitter Creek. At twenty-seven years of age he was still spindly and underdeveloped. His eyes were constantly darting about, like a wary animal's, and in gun battles he would scream each time he fired a bullet. He had one habit that even the outlaws found strange; he never slept under a roof. In all kinds of weather, rain or sleet or snow, he rolled up in a blanket and slept outside.

His explanation was, "My ma jest dropped me in the prairie somewhere and soon after died. Pa broke his rule agin sleepin' under a roof and he got caught. Never seed him again."

Roy Daugherty, alias Tom Jones, nicknamed "Arkansas Tom," ran away from a nagging stepmother who imposed such a stern religious regimen on the home that he constantly found himself in a state of sin. Two of his older brothers studied for the ministry but he revolted and escaped west to become a cowboy. He joined the Doolin gang, no doubt, to strike a blow at his stepmother. She thought he was sinful? He'd prove it to her!

Dan ("Dynamite Dick") Clifton was near forty, the old man of the gang. His specialty was blowing safes. Tilghman, in his notes on Dynamite Dick, wrote ". . . seems to be . . . in good health and active but is said to be afflicted with syphillis. His eyes inflamed on slight exposure, probably in consequence of syphillis . . ."

Charley Pierce was a horse thief from Texas. He was a doltish man whose cheeks always bulged with a cud of tobacco. He seldom spoke words but communicated by the manner of spitting. All he needed was a mouthful of brown saliva in order to express agreement, disagreement, anger, acceptance—the gamut of his emotions.

Jack ("Tulsa Jack") Blake grew up in the Creek Nation where he was a petty thief and hijacker. Joining the Doolin gang put him in the big time and he was always eager to prove his worth by gunning a man down.

There was another member of the gang named Ol Yountis, but he had been killed in November 1892 while raiding the Spearville, Kansas, bank with Doolin.

The gang was composed of emotionally stunted men, driven by fear and hate, vengeful and sadistic. It required a strong man to hold them in check, to make use of them. Bill Doolin was such a man. Statistics of longevity are proof of his skill. The Dalton gang lasted but fifteen months, the Doolin gang was to ravage the frontier for four years.

16

Where to pick up the trail of the Doolin gang? They were last seen in Ingalls, so that had to be the place to start. In this hostile town the presence of a marshal would be immediately reported to Doolin if he was in the area. To overcome this problem Tilghman deputized a man named Morris, a cousin of Madsen's, and two other men who were strangers in the area, and sent the three toward Ingalls. They were to pose as cowmen looking for strays. If they heard anything about Doolin, Morris was to report back to Tilghman's farm in Chandler.

Tilghman, Thomas and Chris Madsen waited on the farm with growing impatience.

"Chris, have they been in there long enough, do you think?" Tilghman asked.

Madsen shrugged his massive shoulders, "A man could be there six months and not learn anything, or he could pick up a lead in six days, six hours, even." He thought a moment. "I don't know what's happened to my cousin, but I think we better move in and have a look."

Tilghman turned to Thomas. "Heck?"

"I agree."

Two days later, after a long and circuitous ride made

mostly at night, the marshals found Morris' camp. He and the other deputies were in a state of excitement.

"We got them, we got them!" Morris exclaimed. "They're living in a dugout on the Dunn ranch. We would have taken them but there were only three of us and the odds seemed long. But now that we're six . . ."

"Wait a minute, Morris," Tilghman said. "Not so fast. Now let's start at the beginning. How do you know the Doolin gang is in this dugout?"

"Picked it up at a saloon in Ingalls. And it figured, because the Dunn brothers have been hiding and feeding outlaws off and on for years. We located the dugout and have kept it under surveillance. One of the Dunn brothers brings food to it twice a day, enough food for six or seven men, I'd say. The outlaws are in there, no question."

"Chris, why don't you take Morris and make a reconnaissance? Be careful."

Within the hour Madsen reported back, "They're in there, all right. Smoke's coming out of a tin stack. It's got a plank roof and a heavy barricaded door. It's dug into the hillside at the end of a ravine. They'd have to come out one at a time, and we could have them covered every step of the way."

"We'll move in on them just before dawn," Tilghman said.

The black sky had turned gray and had the first blush of pink when Heck Thomas called out from the head of the ravine, "Doolin! We know you and your men are in there. You're surrounded by Federal Marshals. Come out with your hands up." There was no response. "Doolin! You got sixty seconds to come out."

Still no response. Thomas took a stick of dynamite from his saddle bag, lit the fuse and threw it. It landed on the hillside above the dugout, exploded thunderously and sent a shower of dirt and rocks down onto the planked roof. "That's dynamite, Doolin," Thomas shouted. "The next stick will be right on your roof. Thirty seconds, Doolin."

There was a creak as the dugout door was swung open and eight men came out to file up the ravine, their hands in the air. Tilghman and Madsen stood at the head of the ravine to disarm each man and peer into his face. When the last man had gone past them, they looked at each other ruefully. There was no Doolin, nor any of his men. The men captured were wanted for a variety of crimes and were handcuffed for the trip back to Guthrie, but the Doolin gang was as far away as ever.

Morris and one deputy loaded the wagon with the prisoners and headed back toward Guthrie. Left to continue the search were "The Three Guardsmen" and the other deputy, a man named Ross. The wagon had just disappeared when a horse and rider appeared on the horizon, traveling hard in their direction. Within minutes the man reined his horse in front of Tilghman.

"You men the law?" he asked.

Tilghman nodded. "United States Marshals."

"You lookin' for Doolin and his gang?"

"Might be. What's it to you?"

"I know where they are. They're headed for Pawnee country. I can point out the trail."

Tilghman studied him for a moment. "What's your name, mister?"

"Lenninger. I got a small ranch south of Ingalls."

"Why do you bring this information to us, Mr. Lenninger?"

"I'm a law-abiding citizen, that's why."

"Good," Tilghman nodded, "I'm glad to hear that. Now, is there any other reason you want Doolin caught?"

The man spoke with some heat. "Yes, by God! They been stealin' my horses and I aim to get even."

Making no effort to prevent the man's hearing his words, Tilghman said to his partners, "This might be a diversion, or even a trap, but we can't ignore it."

Madsen volunteered, "I'll take Ross with me and check it out."

"I intend to have a talk with the Dunn boys," Tilghman said. "We'll make this our base camp."

All that morning Madsen and Ross rode the trail indicated by the rancher, and about noon came upon an Indian's cabin. "Maybe we can get some food here," Madsen said.

As they reined their horses, the door of the cabin opened and out came an Indian, followed by the pungencies of cooking food. He did not seem the least bit surprised to see them. He said, "Dinner all ready."

The horsemen exchanged puzzled looks but said nothing. They dismounted and entered the cabin to eat a simple but generous meal. "What do I owe you for this?" Madsen asked the Indian when the meal was done.

"They say you pay for breakfast, too," the Indian replied.

"Who said what?" Madsen demanded.

"Men who here this morning, eat breakfast. Chief man say you be along high sun, pay for both meals."

"Chief man? Was he tall and skinny with hair the color of wheat?"

"That him! Him say you pay . . ."

Madsen hit the table with his fist. "Doolin, by God! It turned out to be a trap, after all! A trap for a free meal!" Then he began to laugh.

Madsen paid the Indian for both meals, then mounted and headed back toward Ingalls. "We're only a few miles from the Pawnee country," he explained to Ross, "and there are thousands of caves for hide-outs in that area. And since Doolin knows we're on his trail . . . well, we'd never find him."

They rode in silence for a time, then Ross said, "Chris, I don't see why you paid that Indian for the gang's breakfast."

"Well, now, we might be coming this way again some time. And if we do, I'd rather have him a friend than an enemy."

Back at the base camp Madsen reported the events to

Tilghman, who said glumly, "We could take a hundred men into Pawnee country and not find them in those caves."

"How'd you make out with the Dunns?" Madsen asked.

"Cleared out—the two brothers and the three cousins—not a sign of them."

"They'll be back. They gotta tend their cattle."

"I don't propose to wait. They'd only deny feeding those men in the dugout."

Thomas said, "I think we could squeeze one or two of those men enough to get them to testify against the Dunns. We could get a conviction on harboring known criminals."

"Yes," Tilghman admitted, "we could get the Dunns put in jail, but it would take a lot of our time and divert us from our main job—getting Doolin. Besides, I have a feeling that one day they'll be more useful to us out of jail than in it. I'm in favor of giving the Dunns some more rope."

Through that fall and winter the Doolin gang struck time and time again, always retreating safely into the fastness of Indian Territory. On the evening of January 5, 1894, two members of the gang entered the Clarkson Post Office, held up Postmaster Waltman and looted the mail. On January 23 Doolin himself entered the Farmers' and Citizens' Bank of Pawnee, put a gun to the head of Cashier C. L. Berry, and after scooping up the ready cash, marched him out of the bank as hostage. Tulsa Jack and Dynamite Dick were waiting with the horses. Shooting their guns in the air to disperse a curious crowd, they rode out of town with Berry draped over Doolin's saddle horn. The cashier was dumped, unharmed, on the edge of town.

Tilghman kept a record of the Doolin gang holdups and he wrote into his small notebook: *January 23, 1894, Farmers' and Citizens' Bank, Pawnee, $300.*

Heck Thomas looked over his shoulder and observed, "Didn't get much."

"If they got five dollars it's still a success for them and

a failure for us." There was an unaccustomed edge to Tilghman's voice.

"There's just no pattern, Bill."

"Well, there *is* one, in a way. They hit where we least expect them to. If we're looking north, they hit south; if we think they're planning something to the east, they move west. The truth is, they know more about our movements than we know about theirs. Their intelligence system is better than ours, and we've got to do something about it. I think Will Dunn is the key. We get him on our side and we stand a better chance at the gang. I'll have a talk as soon as I get a little more leverage on him."

A few days later Tilghman and Thomas were riding west out of Perry and had a brief encounter which, at the time, seemed without significance. Two horsemen approached them from a mile away. Tilghman pointed them out to Thomas and they both slowed their horses. Accuracy with a gun decreases in ratio to the speed of a horse. As the strangers drew closer the lawmen saw they were heavily armed, each having sidearms plus Winchesters in saddle holsters.

When the approaching horsemen were two hundred yards away, Tilghman chuckled and relaxed. "It's Cattle Annie and Little Breeches."

"Oh, them!" Thomas grinned.

Cattle Annie was an eighteen-year-old girl, daughter of a respectable farmer, who liked to dress up in cowboy clothes and load herself down with guns and ammunition. She was reputed to be a cow and horse thief; it was also said she sold whiskey to the Osage Indians. As yet no one had brought charges against her. She was tolerated as an eccentric of which the frontier community was rather proud. "We got more nuts out here than a pecan factory," was the good-humored boast.

Her partner was a small and slender girl of seventeen, nicknamed Little Breeches. She had been both prostitute and wife. And when her husband discovered that she intended to follow the two careers simultaneously, he returned her to her father in Pawnee. For a time she worked as a domestic but then she met Cattle Annie and they became partners, riding the prairies with all the bravado of real badmen—or badwomen.

When they came opposite the marshals, the men raised their hats gallantly and said, "Ladies." The "ladies" did not respond but rode on by with stony faces.

At one o'clock in the morning of March 13, 1894, Doolin and Dalton rode quietly into the sleeping village of Woodward, a railroad town of some prosperity. The outlaws tethered their horses in front of the railroad hotel, a two-story wooden structure with cell-like bedrooms.

Sounds of laughter and a wash of yellow lantern light spilled across the boardwalk in front of a saloon down the street, but the hotel was dark and silent. A stairway to the second floor clung to the outside of the building and it creaked under the weight of the two men now climbing it. They paused from time to time and listened, but the only sound was laughter from the saloon. They eased open the door at the top of the stairs and entered a dark corridor. Moving with certainty, they opened the third door on the left.

George Rourke, the railroad station agent, awoke with the feeling of cold steel against his neck. It was the barrel of a gun.

"What do you want?" he asked.

"Get dressed," Doolin ordered.

"You've got the wrong man . . ."

"We got the right man, Rourke. Put your pants on."

Moments later three shadowy figures descended the outside stairs. "I'll get my horse from the stable," Rourke suggested. For an answer he received a painful prod in the kidney. He mounted Doolin's horse, the outlaw mounting behind him, and they headed for the railroad station.

In the corner of the ticket office stood a safe, its door

9. Hilarity Roost, an early cabaret in Guthrie, Oklahoma. Entertainment was provided by the four-piece band shown.

10. The stage, performers and orchestra of Guthrie's first vaudeville house, the Club Theatre, housed in a tent.

11. Hell's Half Acre, a tent city in the instant town of Perry, Oklahoma Territory, after the run.

12. The main street of Chandler, Oklahoma, three months after it was opened to settlement, fifty miles from a railroad.

13. Bill Tilghman became Chief of Police in Oklahoma City in 1911 after the arrival of statehood.

14. Bill Tilghman. in his uniform as the Chief of Police of Oklahoma City, with Chris Madsen, another well-known lawman.

15. Bill Tilghman in Cromwell, Oklahoma, in 1924, when he was recalled from retirement to clean up that boom town.

ornamented with delicate traceries in gold and red. "Open it," Doolin ordered.

"I don't know the combination," Rourke replied.

It was such an obvious lie that Doolin didn't bother to argue the point. He cocked his gun, the small click sounding in Rourke's ears like a thunderclap. He dropped to his knees in front of the safe, spun the dial alternately to the right and left, then swung the door open. Inside was a canvas bag heavy with money. Doolin grabbed it up and tossed it to Dalton.

There followed a brief argument over what was to be done with the station agent now that his usefulness had ended. Dalton was for killing him, repeating over and over, "He's a witness, ain't he? He's a witness, ain't he?"

Doolin held out against murder and they finally reached a compromise; they bound and gagged him, rode him out of town to the stockyards, and dumped him.

That canvas sack contained $6540, the payroll for the United States Army's nearby Fort Supply. Upon hearing of this outrage, Secretary of War Daniel S. Lamont in Washington, D.C., sent troops into the area with orders to "forthwith apprehend and arrest" Doolin and his gang. The troops marched up the hill and down the hill, and never found a Doolin.

Bill Tilghman grimly wrote the new statistic into his notebook: *Woodward railroad station, 1 AM, March 13, 1894, $6,540, Army payroll. Doolin and (probably) Dalton. Station master, George Rourke. Unharmed.*

"Heck," he said to his partner, "where were we the day before this happened, on the twelfth? You recall?"

Heck Thomas thought a moment. "I think we was headed into the Glass Mountains."

"Yes, that's right. We got to the mountain and then started back to Guthrie that same evening. You know something, Heck? If we'd gone straight on we'd have been in Woodward the night of the holdup."

"But we didn't. There was no reason to."

"I know . . . I know. I'm just trying to remember back and see if we missed something, some clue as to what was going on. Who'd we see on that ride?"

"Cattle Annie and Little Breeches," Thomas grinned.

Tilghman repeated the names thoughtfully. "Cattle Annie and Little Breeches. I wonder . . ."

"Aw, now, Bill! You're not thinkin' them two nuts got anything to do with Doolin?"

"I seem to remember something, Heck. Weren't those girls seen in the vicinity of Spearville when Doolin and Ol Yountis held up the bank?"

"Well . . ."

"And again, I recall, they were near Cimarron during the train robbery. And now, here they are again in the area of Woodward."

"That doesn't prove . . ."

"It doesn't *prove* anything, but it sure raises a strong suspicion."

Tilghman's suspicion turned to conviction over the next few days as he visited all the general stores in the area. He found that Cattle Annie and Little Breeches had purchased large amounts of ammunition, enough for a small war. Also, they had bought large quantities of food which they hauled away in a buckboard wagon. There was no question in Tilghman's mind that these girls were Doolin's scouts, lookouts and purchasing agents. It was essential that they be removed.

"I'm going to arrest them," Tilghman announced to Thomas and Madsen.

"On what charge, Bill?" Madsen asked.

"Horse thieves. And I have a case that will stick in court."

Tilghman rode the countryside searching for the girls. "Have you seen Cattle Annie or Little Breeches?" was the question he asked time and again. At last he got a lead; the girls were reported to be living on a farm outside of Pawnee. With Deputy Steve Burke at his side, Tilghman found the house and rode slowly toward it.

"I never arrested a lady before," Burke announced. "Least-ways, not one packin' a gun. A couple of dance hall girls, once, but all the weapons they had was fingernails. Can be right dangerous, fingernails. I remember a time . . ."

Burke's nervous monolog was cut short when the front door of the farmhouse was jerked open and Little Breeches raced out to vault onto her horse and head into the prairie. Tilghman took after her, calling to Burke, "You get the one inside."

As the distance closed between them, Little Breeches began firing over her shoulder at Tilghman. He had no appetite for a gun battle with a seventeen-year-old girl, but neither did he want to be the victim of a lucky shot on her part. He lifted his Winchester, took careful aim and killed her horse.

As the horse fell, Little Breeches lost her gun, but when Tilghman dismounted she went at him with claws extended, screaming her hate. She bit and scratched and kneed him, and he was a battered man when he finally pinned her arms and tied them.

Back at the farmhouse, Cattle Annie had jumped through a window on top of Burke, but he disarmed her before she could shoot him.

The two girls were tried as horse thieves before Judge A. G. Bierer of the 4th Judicial District of Oklahoma Territory. Annie McDougal (alias Cattle Annie) and Jennie Metcalf (alias Little Breeches) were found guilty and sentenced to ten years imprisonment at the Farmington Reform School in Massachusetts. They were defiant to the end, gloried in their notoriety. They were the first "gangsters' molls" in the young nation's history, and their saga was told in a popular ballad of the day:

There was a fair girl, her father was poor,
An honest and God-fearing man;
But his daughter was lonesome and followed the lure
Of a boy in a bad outlaw band.

Poor Cattle Annie, they took her away,
They put her in prison, nobody knows where;
Poor Cattle Annie, they cut off her hair,
She was a good girl 'til they led her astray.

Cattle Annie jumped out the window, they say,
And shot at the men on her trail;
Little Breeches was caught as she hurried away,
Cattle Annie's brave fighting did fail.

Poor Cattle Annie, they took her away,
They put her in prison, nobody knows where;
Poor Cattle Annie, they cut off her hair,
She was a good girl 'til they led her astray.

17

The imprisonment of Cattle Annie and Little Breeches was a blow to Doolin. These girls had been his eyes and ears, his scouts, even his supply troops; without them his ability to outguess Tilghman was compromised. Also, he now did something no man in his position should have done—he fell in love with a respectable girl and married her. She was the daughter of an itinerant preacher who rode a circuit out of Ingalls.

When the gang heard of this event they assumed that the new Mrs. Doolin would undertake the job previously assigned to Cattle Annie and Little Breeches—but not at all! Doolin built a log cabin outside of Ingalls for his bride and gave instructions that none of the gang members should ever visit her, or talk of her, or compromise her in any manner. Even he, Doolin, took the most elaborate precautions when visiting; arriving after sundown and leaving before dawn.

There was some grumbling in the gang, especially from Bill Dalton. "Who does he think she is, too good to associate with the rest of us? Well, maybe *he's* too good for us, too. Maybe he's losin' his guts, wants to quit and become a plow-hand."

He never said this to Doolin, face-to-face, but it was

reported back to the gang leader. Doolin chose to ignore it for the time being, but he knew that the two of them could not travel together much longer.

On April 1, 1894, Dalton and Bitter Creek held up T. H. Carr's general store on the edge of the Seminole Nation. In the gun battle that followed, Carr, a part-time marshal, was killed. When Doolin heard this he was furious, for the killing of a lawman was trouble compounded.

During the first week of May 1894, the gang invaded South West City, Missouri, a farm and mining center on the edge of the Ozark Mountains. It was to be a show-off raid, intended to spread the legend of the Doolin gang's invincibility.

The show didn't quite go according to the script. The bank was successfully looted of $4000, but when the gunmen backed into the street, they discovered that the citizens hadn't been intimidated but had armed themselves and now laid down a withering fire. It was Coffeyville all over again, with the gang forced to fight every inch of the way. The town sheriff was wounded in the thigh, Little Bill Raidler killed Joe Seaborn, a civic leader, Doolin himself was wounded over his left eye.

After escaping, the gang holed up to lick its wounds, and the inactivity worked on their nerves. Dalton stayed drunk, sipping constantly from a jug of scalding Ozark "moonshine." He became maudlin, full of self-pity. He recalled the days of respectability back in California when he could even dream of being elected governor. He bewailed Coffeyville and all that it had done to him and his family. He shed drunken tears when he remembered the wife and children he had left in California. He had turned outlaw to get rich and reclaim his family and move them to Canada, but even that had gone wrong. This gang was his by right of inheritance, but he had been cheated by Doolin. He was ordered about, patronized by the usurper and he didn't know what to do about it—except get drunk.

Doolin watched the degeneration of the man and decided

the time had come to dispose of him. It was simply done. He evolved a new organizational structure under which he would never commit all his men to any single operation. He would make up each raiding party according to the talents of the men and the job to be done. And between jobs he wanted his men scattered and living apart until he again summoned them.

Now recovered from his head wound, Doolin explained the new procedure to his men. Then he shook hands with each of them and said, "I'll see you soon." He mounted his horse and reminded them, "No large group. Travel in pairs."

Two by two the men mounted and rode off, until there was but one left, Bill Dalton. No one offered to ride with him. He realized now, with great bitterness, that Doolin would never again send for him—he had been dumped.

His first reaction was to ride after Doolin and demand an explanation, but he knew it would be useless. Doolin would deny dumping him, and how could he prove it? It was something his bones knew, but that was not sufficient evidence to face his enemy. His second reaction was anger— by God, he'd show them! He'd organize a new Dalton gang. He turned his horse southward and rode into Texas.

On May 23, 1894, Bill Dalton led a ragtag bunch of drunken gunmen into Longview, Texas, and robbed the First National Bank of $2000, killing several men in the process. He holed up in a house outside of Ardmore and each day drank himself to numbness. On June 8 a posse of nine men surrounded the house and demanded surrender. Bill jumped out of a window and made a run for it. Marshal Loss Hart killed him with a single .44 slug.

Doolin's problem had thus been solved.

On January 6, 1895, a bitter cold day, Tilghman and Deputy Neal Brown set out from Guthrie in a covered wagon containing a month's supply of food. On their second day out a northeast wind descended on the plains, whipping the snow into blinding clouds and flinging them against the horses and the two men huddled on the wagon seat. At noon the sun was but a pale disk without warmth or light, and they were lost.

At about three o'clock Tilghman reined up and pointed ahead. "You see anything over there, Neal?"

Brown peered through the snow. "A dugout?"

"A dugout with smoke coming out the chimney. A fire!"

"I don't see any horses about, Bill," Brown said.

"Must be someone in there to build a fire. I'll go see if he'll share it with us."

Tilghman descended the few steps to the heavily planked dugout door. He knocked, then pushed it creakingly open. At the far end of the room was a fire of blackjack logs. Along the two sides was a double tier of bunks, each curtained by burlap. On an upturned log in front of the fire sat a man cleaning a rifle. As his eyes became accustomed to the gloom, Tilghman recognized him as a cousin of the Dunn brothers. Whether the man recognized him or not, Tilghman couldn't tell.

"I was looking for Will Dunn," Tilghman said.

The cousin made no response. He did not consider Tilghman's words to be a question.

"Will once said that his fighting dog could whip mine," Tilghman said. "I just happened to be passing this way and thought we could arrange a match."

Still no response from the cousin. Tilghman worked his way around to warm his back by the fire. He looked down the long line of bunks and discovered something had changed. From beneath the burlap curtain on six of them the barrel of a gun poked out, all aimed at him. Had they been there when he entered? Had the guns just been casually tossed on the bunks, or were there men behind them?

Tilghman moved to the other side of the fire, and each gun moved to follow him. There were men behind them!

Rubbing his hands briskly, Tilghman said, "Well, if Will isn't here I might as well move on."

Tilghman made his way toward the door with determined

casualness. His only defense was innocence. If he hurried but one step they would shoot him down. He made it to the door, opened it, stepped outside and closed it behind him. Immediately six men slid from their bunks. There was Red Buck, Dynamite Dick, Tulsa Jack, Charley Pierce, Little Bill and Doolin himself. Red Buck ran for the door.

"Wait!" Doolin called after him.

"That was Tilghman!" Red Buck cried. "This is our chance to get him."

"He's probably out there with a gun aimed at the door."

"He doesn't even know we're here. This is our chance to get him while he's walking away."

"He's too good a man to shoot in the back," Doolin said.

Red Buck's bloodshot eyes opened wide in disbelief. His face flushed, his mouth went slack. Finally he was able to choke out, "Too . . . too good a man . . . ?" Then he turned and started again for the doorway.

"Grab him!" Doolin snapped.

Red Buck fought against the restraining hands but could not break free. He snarled at Doolin, "You're a coward. A yellow-bellied coward." He looked bitterly at the men holding him, and said, "You're all yellow." By including the entire gang in his charge of cowardice he had saved Doolin from the necessity of a personal showdown.

Doolin said calmly, "We'll have a face-to-face fight with Tilghman before long. You'll get your chance." To the others he said, "Hold him while I go out and have a look. We may be surrounded by Federals."

When Tilghman had closed the door he ran for the wagon, calling to Brown, "Hand me my Winchester."

"What's going on?"

"There's a half dozen men hiding down there. I don't know who they are, but they're outlaws. I'll keep the place covered while you go round up a posse."

Brown gestured toward the blinding, swirling snow that blanketed the landscape. "Go *where?* We don't know north from south. If I left you here I might never find my way back."

"We have to take that chance."

"Damn it, Bill, if I left you alone in this storm without shelter you'd be dead before anybody found you. Get in the wagon and we'll both go get a posse."

"I hate to leave them . . ."

"They're not going any place. You don't see any horses. They're in there for the duration of the storm."

Reluctantly, Bill climbed into the wagon and cracked a whip over the team. By the time Doolin stuck his head out the door there was nothing to be seen but the white storm.

18

The two marshals were lost in the blizzard all through that night. When dawn came the wind let up and the snow stopped, and they made a brief camp to rest and feed the horses. Neal Brown looked at the white, featureless landscape and said, "I have no idea where we are, and even less where that dugout was last night."

"Has to be on Dunn land. That was a cousin sitting in front of the fire."

"By the time you add Bee Dunn's land to Will Dunn's land, and then add each of the three cousins' land, there's a fair piece of territory."

Tilghman nodded, then studied the horizon. "I think Will Dunn's ranchhouse should be that way, northwest. Let's head for it."

"You won't be able to raise a posse at Dunn's!"

"I don't think we could raise a posse this side of Guthrie," Tilghman said ruefully. "But the time has come to have a heart-to-heart talk with Will."

By the time the wagon reached the Dunn ranchhouse the afternoon sun was throwing long blue shadows from paddock and barn. Will Dunn came slowly out of the house. He was a square, weathered man with an impassive face, and his attitude was neither welcoming nor hostile, it was watchful.

"I don't trust him," Brown said to Tilghman. "I'll stay back by the wagon and cover you."

Tilghman nodded his agreement, then walked up to the rancher. "Afternoon, Will," he said.

"How do," came the muttered reply.

This seemed sufficient conversation for several moments while the men studied each other. Tilghman broke the silence. "Last night I stumbled in on a half dozen outlaws holed up in one of your dugouts."

"That so? I don't know nothin' about it."

"It's on your land."

"I ain't responsible ever' time a drifter throws a bedroll on my land."

"You knew they were there because you gave them permission. You even sent them food by way of your cousin. You've been harboring known criminals."

There was only the slightest hesitation on Dunn's part. "You can't prove that," he said.

"I think I can, Will. Also, we got a cattle charge against you. I could put you in jail."

"You aimin' to try?"

"I don't know. And that's the truth. I just haven't decided."

As far as Tilghman could judge, the threat of arrest hadn't moved Dunn one way or another. He tried another tack.

"You got a nice spread here, Will. Good land, good strain of cattle. You're building up something a man could be proud of, pleased to pass on to his children. Two boys and two girls?"

"Three boys and a girl," Dunn murmured, his face flushed slightly.

"Oh, yes. Fine lads, I hear, and a pretty girl. Be a shame if you got yourself really crossways and lost all this. Your children deserve better than that."

"What the hell do you want out of me, Tilghman?" Dunn flared.

"I want you to do the right thing, the right thing for yourself and your family. Time's run out on you, Will, and you gotta make a choice. Either you throw in with the outlaws all the way, or you join the decent people in hunting them down. You can't have it both ways—not any longer. Think it over, Will."

Three days later Tilghman walked into Marshal Nix's office in Guthrie to report the events at the dugout. "I returned with a small posse yesterday," he said, "but they had scattered. I don't know for certain who they were. Could have been Doolin men."

"Could have been," Nix nodded.

"Ev, I want to deputize the Dunn brothers," Tilghman said.

His chief looked at him in amazement. "You mean Will and Bee Dunn?"

"Yes, sir."

"Have you gone crazy? They're practically outlaws themselves."

"I know, but . . ."

"There's a cattle rustling charge against them in Pawnee County, and the Federal Attorney here in Guthrie is ready to make a 'harboring' charge against them. And you want to deputize them?"

"I do, and let me tell you why. Our biggest problem has been getting reliable information. The Dunns are in a perfect position to keep us informed where Doolin is and where he plans to go."

"The Federal Attorney wouldn't hear of it, Bill. I'm sorry but it's out of the question."

It wasn't out of the question as far as Tilghman was concerned. The following week he returned to Nix's office to announce that both the Pawnee sheriff and the Federal Attorney had agreed to the plan.

Nix sighed. "Okay, Bill, I'll deputize them if that's what

you want, but I don't like it. You've placed your life in their hands. What's to prevent Will Dunn from leading you into an ambush?"

"One thing, Ev; he *wants* to go straight."

On the evening of April 3, 1895, a Rock Island train was highballing south through Oklahoma Territory toward Texas. Besides the engine and tender, the train consisted of three passenger cars filled with cattlemen coming home from the markets, and one combination express and mail car that contained $50,000 in cash. There were two postal men in the mail car, an oldtimer and a youth making his first trip. Both wore sidearms, and both were nervous, though the old man tried to conceal the condition by bravado.

"Ain't this the middle of the outlaw territory?" the youth asked, peering out the half-open sliding door on the side of the car.

"It be," the old man said.

"I'll be glad when we get through it."

"You got nothing to worry about, kid."

The boy jerked his thumb impatiently toward the far end of the car where there was a pile of heavy canvas money sacks. "I got fifty thousand dollars worth of worries."

The old man hitched his gun belt a bit higher on his hips and boasted, "I been railroadin' thirty years and you know how much I lost? Nothin'. Zero!"

"You was probably never held up, that's why."

The old man brushed this non-essential aside and snapped, "That's gov'ment money in them sacks. It's payroll for the U. S. Army forts in Texas. No outlaw is gonna take it and pick a fight with the whole U. S. Army."

It was night and the train was south of Dover in Arapaho land when the engineer saw that the track ahead was barricaded with logs. He hit the brakes hard and as the train slowed, the locked wheels screeching, a masked man rode up beside the open door on the mail car and swung himself aboard. He disarmed the two guards, tossing their guns into the night, then tossed the money bags to other masked horsemen waiting outside. Within five minutes the money and the masked men were gone.

"The Doolin gang," the old man shrilled. "I recognized them, by God, the Doolin gang!"

He hadn't recognized them at all, but if he had to be held up there was a certain triumph in having it done by the best, the most notorious. In fact, it *was* the Doolin gang, and after the holdup they rode west into the sandhills.

At daybreak a special train arrived at the scene of the crime and out of it poured Deputy U. S. Marshals Madsen, Prater and Banks, two Indian scouts, and three possemen recruited in El Reno. Their horses were unloaded from a boxcar and they mounted to take up the trail that was five hours old.

They followed the trail of hoof marks and droppings as it ran northwest to Hoil Creek in Major County. At two in the afternoon they topped a small hill; in the valley beyond they saw the Doolin gang resting in a stand of stunted blackjack. Tulsa Jack was the first to spot the approaching posse and shouted a warning as he raced for his horse. Deputy Banks took careful aim and drilled him at the base of the skull. Tulsa Jack flopped on the ground and never moved again.

Seeing it was dangerous to leave the shelter of the trees, the outlaws dug in for a siege. Madsen deployed his men in a semicircle on the rim of the small valley and poured a withering fire down on Doolin, Red Buck, Bitter Creek and Charley Pierce. The trees protected the gang, however, and more than two hundred shots were exchanged without a second casualty.

After forty-five minutes of the stalemate, Doolin ordered his men to make a run for it. Red Buck was the first to mount his horse, and it was promptly shot from under him. He vaulted up behind Bitter Creek on his horse and they all rode hell-for-leather down the far end of the valley, bullets winging around them but making no hits.

Deputies Banks and Prater took Tulsa Jack's body back to Guthrie, Madsen led the rest of the posse after the fleeing gang. Doolin had decided to retreat into the Cherokee Strip, the traditional haven of outlaws, but he was slowed by a long delayed showdown with Red Buck Weightman, the most vicious of his men.

At about noon the gang had come upon a cabin with a barn and a small corral containing a good-looking saddle horse. Red Buck, who was riding behind Bitter Creek, said, "Hold up. Here's where I get me a horse."

He slipped to the ground, ran into the barn and soon came out dragging a saddle, blanket and bridle. Taking a lariat from the saddle horn he lassoed the horse and began to saddle it when the door of the cabin opened and an old man came out. He wore an ancient Prince Albert coat, shiny from use, and the frayed shirt flapped dispiritedly as he tried to run on brittle legs.

"Mister!" he called. "That horse belongs to my son."

Red Buck whirled toward him, gun in hand.

The old man stopped, then said mildly, "No need to pull a gun on me. I'm a preacher of the Lord's Word, and I love . . ."

Red Buck shot him, the bullet entering the center of his thin chest. He fell jerkily to the ground, like a marionette whose strings have been cut.

"You damn fool!" Doolin burst out. "There was no need to kill the old man."

"No need not to," Red Buck drawled. He held his gun loosely in his hand, his eyes watchful.

The muscles in Doolin's jaw twitched as he fought for control of himself. Finally he said in a flat voice, "Get on that horse and let's get the hell out of here."

They rode until their horses were blowing, then Doolin called a halt. "Empty the saddle bags," he ordered.

Onto the ground went the canvas money bags looted

from the train. Doolin divided it up, each man receiving an equal share. When Red Buck received his bag of money, Doolin moved quickly to disarm him, then stepped back, covering him with his own gun.

"All right, you stupid sonofabitch," Doolin said, "we're quits. Mount up and ride out of here."

Red Buck looked to the others, but he found no support.

"Ride!" Doolin snapped.

Red Buck shrugged, put the money in his saddlebag and rode off.

19

A stranger walked into the United States Marshal's office in Guthrie on the afternoon of April 28 and said to Tilghman and Nix, "I know where four members of the Doolin gang are hiding."

"Where?" Nix snapped. He was accustomed to a parade of crackpot informers passing through his office and he seldom took them seriously.

"Bitter Creek, Little Bill, Dynamite Dick and Charley Pierce," the man said.

Tilghman showed more interest than his boss. He swung his chair around to face the stranger squarely and said, "Just where are these men?"

"At Bee Dunn's ranch."

"How do you know?" Nix demanded.

The man leaned close, gave a conspiratorial wink, then peeled off part of his artificial mustache. "I'm Will Dunn," he grinned.

"I'm damned," Tilghman exclaimed. "I didn't recognize you, Will." Tilghman turned to introduce him. "Marshal Nix, this is Will Dunn, one of our deputies."

Nix grunted, avoided shaking hands. "Why all the disguise?" he demanded.

Dunn laughed, unoffended. "You don't expect me to enter

the U. S. Marshal's office with my own face showing!"

"What's this about the Doolin gang, Will?" Tilghman asked.

"Bitter Creek and Little Bill been off at Chicago for the last month, livin' high. Now they're broke again. Little Bill spent the last of his money on a pair of silver-plated six-shooters with ivory handles. He says he's anxious to break them in."

"Dynamite Dick and Charley Pierce? What plans do they have?"

"They don't know. None of them know. They're just waitin' for Doolin to send for them."

"And they're all holed up at your brother's ranch?"

"Well, they left this morning but they're coming back by the end of the week."

"You're *sure?*" Nix growled.

Dunn shrugged his shoulders. "How can anybody be *sure* about anything? They said they'd be back and I think they will."

Nix said, "Wait outside for a few minutes. I walk to talk to Marshal Tilghman."

When they were alone Nix said, "How do you see it? He telling the truth?"

"I think so."

"It might be a trap."

"It might be."

"I'd hate to see you take the chance of being ambushed."

"The way I see it, Ev, we don't dare *not* take a chance. If we bag these four, the back of the Doolin gang is pretty well broken."

Nix sighed. "I suppose you're right. But watch yourself on this one."

Within an hour Tilghman, Heck Thomas, Will Dunn and three possemen rode quietly out of Guthrie and headed toward Bee Dunn's ranch. When they arrived they found the owner leaning on a corral fence, his face impassive until he saw his brother in the middle of the posse.

"What in hell you doin' there, Will?" Bee asked.

Tilghman cut in, "Bee, we know you been sheltering some of Doolin's men. We know they're coming back here."

"You tell him that, Will?" Bee demanded.

"It doesn't make any difference who told us," Tilghman said, "the fact is that we know. And now you have a choice— you can help us or not help us take those outlaws."

"You got a price tag there some place, ain't you, Marshal?"

"You might call it that. I got a warrant for your arrest on the charge of cattle rustling. If you help us, I'll see that the charge is set aside. If you don't help us, I'll see you stand trial."

"You thrown in with them, Will?" he asked his brother.

Will nodded. "A man would be a fool not to."

Bee shrugged. "Looks like I don't have much of a choice."

"If we get any of them, the reward goes to us," Will Dunn said to his brother.

"That's right," Tilghman said.

"Dead or alive," Will said.

"Dead or alive," Tilghman nodded. "Now show me the inside of the ranchhouse."

It was a two-story wooden house, the second floor being a single-room barracks with bunks for fifteen men. After the tour of inspection, Tilghman said to Heck Thomas, "Windows to the north, west and south."

"The east ones boarded up," Thomas said. "That's our blind side."

"No telling what direction they'll come from. We'll have to cover the east from outdoors."

Thomas squinted at the sky just beginning to turn pink in the west. "About one hour of light. Time enough to throw up a bunker to the east."

Shovels were produced and within thirty minutes a pit was dug deep enough to conceal three men.

"I'll take the pit tonight," Thomas volunteered to Tilghman, the two of them standing apart from the rest of the men. "Who should I take with me?"

"It might be well to separate the Dunn brothers," Tilghman said softly. "Suppose you take Bee Dunn, I'll keep Will with me in the house. And Heck, let's take Bitter Creek and the rest of them alive if we can. But on the other hand, I don't want to lose any of our men. We'll give them a warning shot in the air and then a call to surrender."

"And if they don't?"

Tilghman sighed, "We'll do what we must."

It was a cold night and a cheerless dawn. It began to rain. There was no sign of the outlaws that day, or the next. On the evening of the third day a shadow appeared in the east. Was it a man? After more than forty-eight hours of vigilance, of straining every nerve to see across the empty plains, the fatigued lawmen were not certain what was shadow and what substance.

The shadow grew larger and separated. It was a man, all right. It became two men on horseback. They came from the east and no one inside the house would see them; it was all up to the men behind the bunker—Heck Thomas, Bee Dunn and a posseman.

"What do you make of it, Bee?" Thomas asked.

"I think . . . it's Bitter Creek and Charley Pierce."

"See any sign of Little Bill? Or Dynamite Dick?"

"Nope . . . not yet."

By now the outlaws were less than a hundred yards away and riding easy. "No killing if we can avoid it," Thomas instructed. "At my signal make the first shot in the air."

The horsemen were fifteen yards away when three shots rang out. "You're surrounded!" Thomas yelled at them. "Throw up your hands."

The startled horses reared and their riders, cursing and pulling their guns, dismounted and ran toward the bunker where they had seen the flashes of gunfire. As they neared the earthen ramparts they must have known death was

waiting there, yet they came on, firing wildly. Both had
sworn to die rather than be captured and jailed, but it
was not that vow that drove them now, they had no time
to think of that. Their nerves and muscles were responding
automatically. They were primitive men who solved their
problems by quick, unthinking violence.

The men behind the bunker saw the death charge,
leveled their rifles and cut the attackers down. Charley
Pierce fell first, and as he lay dead on the ground his head
was barely one foot short of the bunker. Handsome Bitter
Creek Newcomb lay sprawled but a step behind.

The gunfire had brought Tilghman and the other possemen running from the house. They stood in a large circle
to look down on the two dead outlaws.

"Bitter Creek and Charley Pierce," Thomas said.

"It was necessary to kill them?" Tilghman asked of Heck
Thomas. His tone was not critical, merely a question.

"It was them or us," Thomas answered.

Tilghman nodded. "No sign of Little Bill or Dynamite
Dick?"

"No sign. If they're out there, the gunfire will keep 'em
from coming in."

"Marshal," Bee Dunn said in a wheedling voice, "about
the reward . . ."

Tilghman said coldly, "Put the bodies in a wagon and
deliver them to Nix in Guthrie. He'll pay your bounty."

Tilghman's insistence on using the Dunns had paid off,
but not as handsomely as he had hoped. Yet, even the
elimination of two men constituted considerable inroads on
Doolin's manpower. In 1892 Doolin had a gang of ten
men; now, three years later, he had but three—there were
Dynamite Dick Clifton, Little Dick West, and Little Bill
Raidler.

When Tilghman and Heck Thomas returned to Guthrie
they found themselves heroes. The public had been so excited about the gun fight at Dunn's ranch that Nix had

ordered the funeral parlor opened and the dead gunmen put on display in their caskets. His avowed motive was to use the corpses as an object lesson for any young man who thought an outlaw's life was glamorous.

Tilghman could not walk down the street without dozens of admirers and well-wishers shaking his hand and clapping him on the back. Among them was O. D. Halsell, the rancher who had once employed Doolin as a cowboy.

"Congratulations, Marshal," he said. "Looks like you're closing in on Doolin, all right."

"I hope so."

"You know, Tilghman, Billy Doolin ain't a bad kid."

"He's a killer, Mr. Halsell."

"Yes, yes, I know. I didn't mean it the way it sounded. He *is* a bad one, of course, but I got a fondness for him anyway. No logic to that, I guess, but there it is. I keep remembering what an eager kid he was when he came to work for me, how he wanted to learn about everything. And I keep wondering if I didn't do something wrong to make him turn out this way."

"I wouldn't blame myself if I were you."

Halsell seemed to ponder that for a moment, then said, "He's got a baby son."

"I heard."

"His health ain't very good."

"Better than some," Tilghman said, glancing across the street at the funeral parlor.

"If I was to run into him and I tried to talk him into giving himself up, what could I say? What arguments?"

"The only one I can think of is, if he doesn't give himself up he's sure a good candidate for display at the funeral parlor."

"Anything else I could say?"

"You mean a promise from me? A deal?"

Halsell shrugged. "Anything."

"Decent treatment and a fair trial. That's all I can promise."

"I suppose it is, under the circumstances. Well, I'll tell him the way things are, if I see him."

As he turned to walk on down the street, Tilghman called, "I hope you're not hiding him at your ranch, Mr. Halsell. Harboring a criminal is against the law."

"No, I'm not hiding him," Halsell said.

The following day Halsell met Doolin in a stand of cottonwood north of his ranch. Doolin's face was lined beyond his years, and was of poor color. Though he knew he was safe with his old employer, who treated him like a son, his eyes constantly searched—it was an occupational tic.

"Billy, you look done in," Halsell said.

"I'm all right."

"You need rest."

"I get rest."

Halsell tried another tack. "When was the last time you saw your baby son?"

Doolin's face altered in some mysterious way, the harsh planes on it seemed to soften, and for a moment his eyes came to rest. "Last night, about midnight, I was able to sneak in and see him sleeping in his crib. I don't like to brag, but that kid . . ." his voice trailed off.

"When was the last time you saw him awake, in the daytime, learning to walk and talk?"

"Goddam it, Halsell, don't bait me!" Doolin flared.

"I'm not trying to bait you, Billy, I'm just trying to get you to face a few facts. Your son deserves to have a father around all the time, not just at midnight once a month. You can still salvage part of your life, Billy. Give yourself up and ask the court for mercy. You'll probably get off with a moderate sentence and when you get out of jail you'll be free, you'll be a full-time father."

"A moderate sentence? *Me?* More likely the rope."

"Now, Billy . . ."

"Look at the killings they got me charged with. That big politician named Seaborn in South West City, the sheriff at

Canadian, Texas, the express messenger, the three marshals at Ingalls. And a few others beside."

Halsell heard a boastful tone in the words and he shook his head sadly. "Billy, Billy . . . they'll shoot you down."

"I can take care of myself," Doolin said, patting his holstered gun.

"There's one man who can kill you."

The flat tightness returned to Doolin's face. "Tilghman," he said softly.

20

After his talk with Halsell, Doolin disappeared. No one knew where he was; not Halsell, not his wife, and not Tilghman. Tips and gossip about wanted men flowed constantly into the U. S. Marshal's office in Guthrie, but there was none about Doolin.

Information did come in about Little Bill Raidler. This college man from Pennsylvania, this self-proclaimed intellectual who quoted Chaucer, was reported to be hiding out at the Moore ranch on Mission Creek in the eastern part of Osage country. It was about two hundred miles north and east of Guthrie, but the tip seemed reliable enough to warrant a trip up there. There was also the chance that Doolin was with Raidler. Tilghman saddled up and rode north.

When he arrived at the isolated ranchhouse on a late afternoon he learned that Raidler was hiding in a nearby woods during the day and came into the house only for supper and to sleep. The Moores were technically guilty of harboring a criminal, but like so many ranchers on the frontier, they had no choice. The law was far away, an abstraction; the reality was the outlaw with gun in hand.

As he talked to Moore and his wife, two plain, hardworking people, Tilghman tried to judge where their loyalties really lay. Were they glad he had come to relieve them of the gangster? Or was there some rebellion in them, too, some bitterness at the hard life they led, some personal attachment to the man hiding in the woods? At the moment of showdown, would they help the law, or the outlaw?

They answered Tilghman's questions readily enough, but in monosyllables. They neither concealed nor volunteered information, and Tilghman concluded that they would remain neutral during the contest, siding with the winner.

Tilghman toured the yard, carefully noting the placement of the outbuildings. Raidler would be coming from the west, and before he arrived at the ranchhouse he would pass a corral, a toolshed, and an unchinked log henhouse. By standing flat in the henhouse doorway Tilghman would command the approaches from the west, and at the same time be shielded from any crossfire that might possibly come from the Moores in the ranchhouse.

As the sun began its sudden drop in the west Tilghman instructed the Moores to remain inside the house, then took his own position in the henhouse doorway. For a time the hens clucked and rustled, protesting the presence of a stranger, but as the twilight deepened they settled themselves for sleep.

Then, from a distance, there came the soft *clop-clop* of a horse's hoofs striking the prairie grass. The rider was in no hurry, nor was he being cautious, he was letting the horse set its own pace. Against the last flush of the dying sky, Tilghman saw the silhouette of horse and rider—it was Little Bill Raidler, all right. The outlaw dismounted in the corral, took the saddle and bridle off his horse and draped them on the fence rail, then sauntered toward the house.

"Raidler! This is Tilghman. Throw up your hands."

Raidler drew and whirled, snapping off a quick shot. The bullet grazed Tilghman's head, knocking off his hat, and he triggered one barrel of the shotgun he held leveled. Raidler reeled and staggered, dropped to his knee, all the time firing wildly. Tilghman withheld his own fire and watched Raidler finally pitch forward on his face.

Tilghman approached cautiously until he was able to kick the fallen man's gun away, then bent down to examine him. Raidler was alive.

"Moore!" Tilghman shouted toward the house. "Heat some water and bring some clean cloths." When the makeshift bandages arrived, Tilghman dressed the outlaw's wounds.

"Put hay in the back of your wagon and hitch up a horse," Tilghman instructed Moore.

"What fer?" Moore demanded.

"We have to get him to a doctor."

"Nearest doctor is in Elgin, Kansas. You ain't gonna drive all that far? He'll probably die on ya anyway."

"Put the hay in the wagon," Tilghman snapped.

Tilghman drove all through the night, stopping from time to time to bathe Raidler's fevered face in cool water. At dawn he entered Elgin and routed the doctor out of bed to treat his prisoner. He put Raidler on a cot in a Santa Fe baggage car and rode with him south to Guthrie, giving him medicine every hour. He saved Little Bill's life.

The trial was brief and Raidler was convicted of train robbery and given ten years. After six years he wrote to Tilghman asking his assistance in getting a parole. The marshal appeared personally before the parole board to plead the case, putting his own great personal prestige on the line. He got Raidler out of jail and helped him establish a tobacco store where, for the rest of his uneventful life, he sold cigars—and quoted Chaucer.

The jailing of Little Bill reduced Doolin's gang to himself and two—Little Dick West and Dynamite Dick Clifton. It was doubtful that he could command even them, for he had lost the one quality essential for leadership— an aura of invincibility. He was on the run and no one wanted to run with him. Nor did he want them to, for a man can best hide alone.

Cutting loose from Doolin did not save the other two, however. Marshal Heck Thomas led a posse after Dynamite Dick, caught up with him ten miles west of Checotah in the Creek Nation. In the brief gun battle the outlaw was killed.

Little Dick eventually joined the Jennings gang, some of the most inept gunmen in the history of the West. Al and Frank Jennings were soon captured, and Tilghman led a posse after Little Dick who hid out at a farm in Lincoln County just east of Guthrie. In the inevitable gun battle, Little Dick was killed.

As for Red Buck, the bad man banished even by his own kind, he died in a dugout near Arapaho in Cheyenne Territory. He was found and surrounded by a posse and ordered to surrender. When he came out with his gun blazing, the lawmen killed him with the impersonalness of men killing a mad animal.

Cherchez la femme!

Cherchez la femme? Even in a Western wilderness? Tilghman decided to follow the French adage and look for Doolin's wife, Edith. He headed generally north, stopping at every farm and ranchhouse, asking questions, asking, asking.

Though he came upon no hard information, he noticed a change in attitude; the farmers and ranchers were more hospitable, less reluctant to talk. Clearly they had not been recently harassed by outlaws; they no longer feared to cooperate with the law. They had decided which was the winning side, and were ready to join it.

Tilghman had crossed into Kansas before he got any kind of a lead. He was talking to a rancher when the wife spoke up from her rocker on the front porch. "Marshal, do you think this fellow might have settled near Burden, Kansas?"

"I don't know, ma'am. Might have. Why do you ask?"

"Well, I was home visiting my folks last month and heard some talk about a new couple named Wilson."

"What did they say about them?"

"Mostly that they didn't seem too friendly. He built a cabin west of town, then he'd disappear for weeks at a time. She'd drive into town for supplies about once a week and look straight ahead, not speak to nobody but Sam Dixon, who runs the general store."

"Did she have a baby?"

"Yes, come to think of it, she did."

"What did this Mr. Wilson look like?"

"Well, I never seen him with my own eyes, but I hear tell he was rather tall and skinny. And pleasant spoken, whenever he spoke."

Tilghman thanked the rancher and his wife and headed his horse toward Burden. The town was close to two hundred miles east of Ingalls, and 45 miles north of the Kansas-Oklahoma border. It was a frail lead to follow so far, but all that Tilghman had.

It was mid-afternoon days later when Tilghman came upon the cabin outside of Burden. It was in a ravine shielded on three sides by a heavy growth of trees which provided perfect cover for an observer. Tilghman settled down to wait developments. Two hours later he heard the soft *clop-clop* of an approaching horse. Into view came a buckboard driven by a young woman who had a baby on the seat beside her. Tilghman had seen some family pictures and recognized "Mrs. Wilson" as Edith Doolin.

As soon as dark had settled on the ravine, Tilghman crept close to look in a window. The single room cabin was occupied by mother and child alone. There was no way of judging when Doolin had left or when he would come home. Tilghman returned to the woods, spread out a bedroll, and settled down to wait. He waited for seven days, from time to time slipping into Burden to look around, but always returning to his observation point.

The Burden postmaster had been instructed by Tilghman

to watch Edith Doolin's mail, but he found no letters coming from the husband. Her only correspondent turned out to be Mary Pierce, the keeper of the Ingalls hotel and brothel which had once been the Doolin gang's hangout. The letters seemed innocuous enough.

Edith Doolin's trips to town usually resulted in two stops, Sam Dixon's general store for groceries, and the post office for mail. One day she made three stops, the additional one being at the railroad station.

"That young lady that just left here," Tilghman subsequently said to the ticket agent, "did she buy a ticket?"

"Don't 'pear to me that's any of your business," the agent said.

"You're wrong, friend," Tilghman said, producing his badge.

"Oh, yes, sir, I see it is, Mister Marshal. Yes, sir, she bought a ticket."

"To where?"

"To Perry, Oklahoma, sir."

She was apparently going to visit her parents who now lived in Perry. Tilghman sent a wire to Nix, asking that Edith Doolin be kept under surveillance in Perry. Then he packed up his bedroll and headed for Ingalls.

Mary Pierce had two failings (aside from her morals). She liked to talk and she responded to flattery. When Bill Tilghman first checked into her hotel she treated him with great reserve, but slowly thawed. He did say the nicest things, she thought, and such a good listener. He wasn't such a bad fellow—for a lawman.

Several times Tilghman tried to steer the conversation to the subject of outlaws, but the madam always shied away. He began to wonder if he was not wasting his time here. Tomorrow morning he'd bring it to a head, one way or the other.

The morning sun was warm and Tilghman lounged in a front porch rocker, his eyes half-shut. He appeared to be drowsing, but he wasn't. He was waiting.

"Good morning, Mr. Tilghman," Mary Pierce said briskly as she came out on the porch, broom in hand.

"Morning," in a sleepy voice. "Am I in your way?"

"Not at all. I'll just sweep around you."

The cornstalks of the broom made a harsh sound as she swept the rough floor with housewifely vigor. When she finished she leaned on the broom handle and looked down the town's main street where the saloons were already doing business.

"Hear about the train robbery in Texas?" Tilghman asked.

"No, I didn't." She didn't turn around.

"Sounds like Bill Doolin."

Now she swung around, her eyes flashing anger. "Everything that happens is blamed on Doolin, Hell, he ain't even *in* Texas."

"Oh? I heard he was."

"You heard wrong! Last two months he's been at a springs for his rheumatism. I know." She patted a letter that stuck out of her apron pocket.

"Let me see that letter, Mary."

"I will not!"

Tilghman stood up. Gone was his sweet amiability. "I can arrest you any time for harboring criminals. And unless I get some cooperation . . ."

He held out his hand and she put the letter in it. It was from Edith Doolin and had been mailed from Burden on the day she took the train to Perry. The closing paragraph read, "The springs seem to be helping my husband. He sent word that he'll stay for another month."

Tilghman handed the letter back to Mary Pierce, saying, "Hot Springs is good for aches, I hear." He watched her face and saw a tiny smile. He had guessed wrong. Then it would be Eureka Springs, Arkansas—not so famous, not so expensive, and closer!

There was some excitement in the Federal Marshal's office in Guthrie when Tilghman reported in with the information he had worked out of Mary Pierce.

"How many men do you want in Eureka Springs?" Nix asked.

"None," Tilghman answered. "It's best done quietly. I'll go alone."

"Bill, Doolin will shoot you on sight."

"I'll try to persuade him otherwise."

21

On the morning of January 12, 1896, Bill Tilghman stepped off the train at Eureka Springs and walked slowly up the main street toward the Basin Hotel. As a concession to Nix, Tilghman was in simple but effective disguise—he was dressed as an itinerant preacher. He wore a rumpled, long-skirted Prince Albert coat, a derby, and he moved with the dolorous and deliberate manner frequently affected by frontier preachers. The whole aspect was so unlike Tilghman's own that even his intimates would have been momentarily fooled.

Behind his pious expression every nerve was alert, and his eyes constantly searched the wooden walks on each side of the rutted street. Then he saw him! Within minutes after arriving in town he saw Bill Doolin!

There was a change in the man; arthritis had bent him a bit and he walked with the help of a cane. One thing hadn't changed: there was still a bulge in his jacket under his left arm where he carried his .45 in a shoulder holster.

Tilghman pondered how to take him. Doolin had sworn never to be taken alive, and to attempt arrest now on the street would surely result in a gunfight. No, the way to do it was to get close to him and overpower him, prevent his reaching for his gun. This was obviously not the moment to attempt it.

From a distance Tilghman watched Doolin enter a small park, cross a footbridge over a stream, then follow a path to a house set on a hillside, with a sign in the parlor window that read ROOMS FOR RENT. Turning back, Tilghman checked into the Basin Hotel, demanding a room on the second floor, front. For a time he studied the street from his window, then he unpacked and went downstairs for lunch.

After a leisurely meal he stepped outside to again study the town. He was a stranger but did not attract undue attention, for the town was full of strangers—men and women who came to ease a variety of pains by immersing themselves in the mineral baths. Even a preacher could have a pain.

In the middle of the afternoon Bill Tilghman felt unaccountably tired. He was forty-two but in excellent physical condition; his fatigue was of the spirit. He was tired of the hunt. He was tired of having to study each new town with an eye to a gunfight. He was tired of measuring men, not for the good that was in them but for the bad. He had promised himself that he would resign once Doolin was caught and safely jailed.

A sign reading BATHS loomed up before him and he decided to see if the magic waters would ease his kind of ache. He stepped into a square lobby with a small desk by the front door and presided over by a short, bald man. Around the edge of the room were wooden chairs, about half of them occupied. On the back wall was a door marked BATHS, to its right an enormous pot-bellied stove, and to the right of the stove was another wooden chair on which sat Bill Doolin reading a newspaper.

"May I help you, sir?" asked the bald man behind the desk.

Doolin moved his paper aside to look at the newcomer.

"I'll take a bath," Tilghman said gruffly, dropping a half-dollar on the desk. He walked toward the bath door un-hurriedly but on the balls of his feet. Through the door he found himself in a long corridor, and he flattened himself against the wall, whipping out his gun. Had Doolin recognized him? Would he follow through that door?

A minute passed and Tilghman eased the door open a crack. He looked past the stove, and beyond it at Doolin's legs and boots. They were stretched out, crossed at the ankles.

With cat quickness Tilghman leaped through the door and landed squarely in front of Doolin, his gun at the man's forehead. "Put up your hands," he barked.

Arthritis or not, Doolin responded almost as fast. Ignoring the gun held on him, he jumped to his feet and went for his own gun. Tilghman grabbed for his right hand but as Doolin jerked backwards he caught nothing but the end of the right sleeve. The outlaw struggled to free his imprisoned gun hand but Tilghman hung on and the shoulder seam began to part.

"Bill, you know who I am . . . Tilghman. Put up your hands."

Locked together, they struggled around the quickly emptied room. Inch by inch Doolin's hand moved toward his gun. In a moment the sleeve would be torn free.

"Doolin!" Tilghman pleaded, "don't make me kill you."

They looked at each other, and in Doolin's eyes was the rage and fear of a trapped animal. In Tilghman's eyes there were purpose, inflexible will, and a touch of sadness. Doolin had long boasted that he would never be taken alive, but now that he saw death, he hesitated. Slowly the tension went out of his body and he raised his hands in the air. Tilghman took his gun, then turned him to the wall and frisked him for a second weapon. There was none. Turning him back, he slipped the handcuffs on. As they clicked shut, Tilghman sighed. It was done—after four long years, it was done!

"Doolin, are you coming quietly with me?"

"Yes, Marshal. Can I pick up my things? I've got a hundred dollars in the bank, and my clothes in a rented room."

Tilghman looked at his watch. "There's a train out of here at four o'clock. We've got time."

Still Doolin hung back. "Mr. Tilghman, this is lynch country, and we're close to the Missouri border. That bank job we pulled in South West City, a big politician named Seaborn got killed. If any Missouri sheriff claims me, it will be a rope on the first tree over the border." He held up his manacled hands. "You walk me down the street in these cuffs and everybody in town is gonna know who I am."

"What are you proposing, Bill?"

"Let me come along without cuffs and I give you my word I won't cause any trouble."

To take an outlaw's "word" seemed madness, but Tilghman judged his man and removed the cuffs. But with the warning, "If you try anything, Doolin, I'll have to kill you. You know that, don't you?"

"Yes, sir, I know that."

They went to the bank, then to Doolin's room where Tilghman ordered him to stand in a corner while he packed the luggage. On the dresser there was a silver cup. "This yours?" Tilghman asked.

Doolin nodded. "It was a present for my baby son."

"I'll deliver it for you," Tilghman said gently, putting the cup in the voluminous pocket of his preacher coat.

The U. S. Marshal offices in Guthrie had been packed with men for several days, all waiting for a telegram from Tilghman. When he left on Doolin's trail, Nix had said, "When you locate him, Bill, just send me a telegram and I'll send twenty-five deputies to help you take him."

On the morning of January 13 the telegram was delivered into the hands of Nix's chief deputy, John Hale. He quickly tore open the envelope and pulled out the sheet containing the message. Then he did a very uncharacteristic thing—he let out a war whoop. "He's done it!" Hale cried. "Tilghman has captured Doolin!"

Men came pouring in from adjacent offices to make sure they had heard right. "It's true," Hale said, waving the yellow message paper. "Bill captured him in Eureka Springs and is bringing him here on the morning train."

A reporter rushed out of the building and down the street toward the newspaper offices, his coattails flying, every few steps, shouting, "Tilghman has captured Doolin, coming on the morning train!"

Though the train was not scheduled to arrive for three hours, people began pouring down the street to the depot. Within a half hour there were five thousand men, women and children massed around the station, and there was much shouting and laughter. It was a carnival atmosphere for the people believed that this day marked the end of the gangs.

Down the track came a fussy engine pulling a tender and half a dozen wooden coaches. The crowd fell silent as the train came to a shuddering stop, and for a long moment the only sound was the panting of the engine. As Doolin stepped out on the open platform between coaches, a hissing sound swept through the crowd; each man asking his neighbor, "That's him?"

Doolin shrank back, but Tilghman behind him said, "It's not a lynch mob, Bill. They're just curious about you."

The crowd stared at the skinny, stooped figure leaning on a cane and said to itself, "*That's* Doolin, the dangerous outlaw? We've been afraid of *him?*"

As Doolin hesitated, Tilghman said, "Here, I'll go first."

The moment the marshal appeared a great roar went up from the crowd. Five thousand throats shouted his name, cheered. It was a hero's return.

It was with the greatest difficulty that Tilghman and his prisoner made their way through the crowd and to the carriage waiting for them. Men wanted to shake Tilghman's hand, women held up their children so they might see the great marshal and remember this moment in years to come. Once in the carriage, mounted outriders cleared a way through the crowd and led them to the jail. The steel gates closed at last on Bill Doolin.

The buggy trip from the jail back to the marshal's office was again a triumphal parade. People lined the streets to applaud and cheer, treating Tilghman as a sort of liberator. From time to time Tilghman raised his white ten-gallon hat in acknowledgment. Finally in the office, he conferred with Nix and the Federal Attorney about preparations for the trial.

"I'm going to ask for murder in the first," the attorney said. "I'm drawing witness subpoenas for the Dunns, Mrs. Pierce and Oscar Halsell. I'll be going to Ingalls and South West City for more witnesses, maybe Woodward and Clarkson. Who should I look up in those towns, Bill?"

"I don't think you'll need to subpoena anyone," Tilghman said. "Doolin will plead guilty."

"He will?" The Federal Attorney exclaimed, a note of disappointment in his voice. He saw the biggest trial of the decade slipping away from him.

"Doolin has promised me he would plead guilty and throw himself on the mercy of the court."

"He gets a smart-aleck lawyer and he may change his mind."

"I hope not," Tilghman said quietly.

Minutes later the attorney shuffled some papers together, stuffed them in his pocket and left the office. Tilghman looked at his boss and said, "I've done my job, Ev."

"And well done, well done."

"I want to resign."

"Now, Bill . . ."

"My ranch needs attention . . ."

"You forgotten the five thousand dollar reward you got coming? That can hire a lot of ranch hands."

Tilghman grinned. "No, I haven't forgotten the reward, and I don't deny it will come in handy but . . ."

"Bill, I need you."

"Now, Ev, you and I know that I did nothing that Thomas or Madsen or a dozen other men around here couldn't have done."

"The point is, *you* did it. And that makes you a hero. Don't interrupt, hear me out. Remember when we first opened shop over five years ago? Half of the people were for us and half against. Those against us were not really against law and order; they just didn't think we could bring it to Oklahoma and they wanted to be on the winning side. After today there is no question which is the winning side. As long as you're a Federal Marshal we're all invincible in the public eyes. There's some dirty jobs yet to be done, Bill, and they'll be easier done with you around. Now, as a favor to me, don't give a decision on this right now. Think it over for a week or so."

"I'll think it over," Tilghman said.

22

The foreman on Tilghman's ranch, Tom Avery, sat on a corral fence rail and watched his boss approach, riding his horse in an easy, unhurried gait. Avery had heard about the capture of Doolin and he waved a greeting and called, "Congratulations, Bill."

Tilghman slid from the saddle and handed the reins to the foreman. "Thanks," he said with a grin. Then, seriously, "Tom, what would you do around here with five thousand dollars?"

"The reward money? You got it in your pocket?"

"Not yet, but it will be coming along one of these days soon. So, what needs doing?"

"Whew! What *doesn't* need doing?"

"The most important problems. We're overgrazing, aren't we?"

"We sure as hell are! If we're gonna keep the same size herd, we need to fence that north quarter. It's virgin grass and would feed the herd long enough to let the rest of the range recover."

"Good. What else?"

"A bunkhouse—we sure oughta build a bunkhouse. As things is now, I gotta hire the cowhands by the day. They ride out from Guthrie because we got no place to put 'em up. Can't count on any one of 'em returning two days in a row. Now, if we had a bunkhouse . . ."

"Agreed," Tilghman interrupted. Then, changing the subject, he asked, "Tom, how is Mrs. Tilghman?"

"Well . . ."

"I want the truth. Is her cough better?"

"Well, now . . . I wouldn't say it was. No. She don't come out of the house much, but I can hear her coughin'."

"Would you say it's getting worse?"

"Bill, don't ask me that kind of question. I ain't no doc. I don't know if she's better or worse."

At this point the door to the house was flung open and the three children still at home (William, Jr., Dorothy and Vonia) came running to greet their father. They had intended to throw themselves into his arms but when they were within a couple of yards of him they stopped and stood rather diffidently just out of reach. They did not know him well, to be sure, but their shyness came also from the fact that he was now a hero. They studied him to see how he was different.

Tilghman stepped up and kissed the two girls on the cheeks and shook hands with ten-year-old Billy. It was all quite formal.

"Dad, did you capture Doolin single-handed?"

"Yes, Billy."

"Did you have to shoot him?"

"No."

"Didn't he fight at all?" The boy was disappointed.

Tilghman ruffled his son's hair, grinned at him affectionately and said, "Yes, he did fight, Billy. I had to subdue him and put handcuffs on him. I'll tell you all about it at supper tonight. I want to see Mama now."

When he walked to the house and entered, the children remained discreetly outdoors. She was sitting by the window from which she had been obviously watching his arrival. She was a delicate woman, still pretty; her cheeks flushed, not from rouge but a fever. He bent to kiss her, but she did not raise her face and his lips brushed only the top of her head.

"Hello, Flora. I'm home for good."

She gave a short, bitter laugh which induced a spasm of coughing. Her face turned scarlet and tears ran down her cheeks and she gasped for air, and all the time Tilghman looked on helplessly.

When the seizure finally ended, Bill said, "You're not well, Flora. I wish you'd let me bring a doctor to see you."

"If I'm sick," she said in a dull voice, "it's only from loneliness and boredom. Why do you do it, Bill?" She looked up at him. "Why do you get a job that keeps you away from home? For a time I thought it was other women . . ."

"Flora!" He was genuinely shocked.

She shook her head. "I don't believe that any more. But what is it? I've never understood."

Tilghman studied his boots. "It's not easy to explain, Flora."

"Try! For God's sake, try!"

"Excitement and danger? Maybe they pull at me a bit, but not much. Not like when I was a young man. I'm forty-two, Flora, and the trail isn't as easy to ride as it once was. No, what used to be adventure is now hard work. But worth it. When I'm out there on the prairie and the wind stirs the sweet smelling grass, I think there is nothing more beautiful in the world. I think of my children and grandchildren living here in peace, loving the prairie the way I do. But there can be no peace while the outlaws ride. I suppose every man wants to leave his mark on the land, wants to turn it over to his children better than he found it. Well, that's my way—fighting the outlaws. I don't know how else to explain it, Flora. That's the best I can do."

There ensued a long moment of silence. Flora, her chin cupped in one hand, stared out the window at the flat and featureless prairie. "I don't see the things you see," she finally said in a small voice. "I've tried, I've tried real hard, but I can't see anything but dust and heat and snow and loneliness. I'm not a pioneer woman, that's all. You married wrong, Bill. I don't reckon either of us is entirely to blame, but there it is. I'll give you a divorce."

"Flora, I've come home to stay."

"I don't believe it," she said flatly. "And if you had any sense you wouldn't believe it either."

The harsh cough seized her, shook her, its violence making her gasp. When it eased off a bit he picked her up and carried her to bed. Then he saddled up and rode to town for a doctor.

The diagnosis was consumption, a disease of the lungs known to later generations as tuberculosis. "Bed rest and plenty of fresh air," the doctor instructed. "And don't let her worry about anything. Keep all bad news from her."

Tilghman looked forward to the arrival of the $5000 reward; he planned to present it to her as an earnest of their new life together. But it didn't come.

Before his trial started Doolin led a jail break and disappeared. Heck Thomas headed a posse which found him outside of Lawson, and in the gun battle that followed, Doolin was shot dead.

The language of the posted reward read: "Five thousand dollars will be paid for the arrest and conviction of William Doolin . . ." Since he was never convicted, the reward was never paid. It made no difference, really. Before the bad news arrived, Flora was dead.

23

The preacher bent down to scoop up a handful of dirt and dropped it in the open grave. It made a hollow thud when it hit Flora Tilghman's casket six feet down. Then he intoned, "Earth to earth, ashes to ashes, dust to dust; in sure and certain hope of the Resurrection unto eternal life."

The mourners, about fifty of them, mounted their horses and buggies for the trip back to the Tilghman farm where they had previously delivered casseroles. There was enough food to feed not only themselves in this traditional post-burial supper but the widower and his motherless children for at least a week to come.

It was late afternoon before the last person had been fed, the dishes washed and stacked by the women, a proper swig of corn liquor taken by the men, and the last buggy clattered down the road. Bill's parents had taken the grandchildren for a few days.

A prairie silence came with the twilight, making the whole land seem mournful. Tilghman leaned on the corral fence and watched the sky darken. Footsteps approached and a shadowy figure leaned on the fence beside him. Tilghman didn't turn his head or speak, for he knew it was Tom Avery. They were friends and comfortable with silence.

Finally, when all was dark except the small red fire in

the bowl of Avery's pipe, Tilghman said, "I can't live here, Tom. Not any more."

Avery made no reply, nor was any wanted. When a man needs to talk, a friend listens.

"She hated this place. I never knew how much until near the end . . . when it was too late. She liked parties, and dancing, lots of people around, but I gave her this." He gestured toward the empty landscape. "Big and free as this land is, for her it was a sort of prison, I guess. I can't understand how she saw things that way, but she did. I have to move out of here, Tom. The place will always remind me of how wrong I was."

"Maybe you was wrong on some things, Bill, but you ain't responsible for her gettin' sick. If you're tellin' yerself that, yer plumb crazy. If she was livin' in Noo York and dancin' ever night, she would have got the consumption just as soon as out here. Probably a sight sooner. You gotta know that!"

"I don't know, Tom. But I appreciate you sayin' it."

"Where you plannin' to go, Bill?"

"I'd like to open a stud farm, breed racing horses. I got a hundred sixty acres on the edge of Chandler that could be used. Might even build my own racetrack. I know where I can buy a couple of good blooded stallions to start with. We could improve our breed as we go along. Will you come with me, Tom?"

"I reckon."

"I'll hire full-time hands, like you want, and we can turn the house into a bunkhouse. How many men do you figure?"

"Five. Mebbe four."

"Let's ride over and take a look at that land."

When word spread that Bill Tilghman was going to establish a stud farm, the citizens of Chandler were delighted. "It'll put us on the map," men said to each other.

The previous year Chandler had suffered a disastrous cyclone and was now painfully repairing the damaged build-

ings. The news that the renowned Tilghman was going to
settle there and breed horses meant that there was a future
for the town. Horses were, after all, the most important single commodity in the whole land. A man's wealth could be
measured not only by cattle and acreage, but also by the
number and quality of his horses. There were no established
stud books in existence and the only assurance a buyer
had that he was receiving blooded stock was the word of
the breeder. And no one ever questioned the word of Bill
Tilghman on *any* subject.

When placing an unusually large order with a dry goods
drummer, one Chandler merchant explained, "Men will be
coming from all over the country to trade with Bill Tilghman. We're in for a boom."

Well aware of his responsibility, Tilghman went to Kentucky for his first studs, dealing with men who kept their
own careful bloodline records. He bought two stallions, drove
them back to his farm, and then printed his first catalog.
The cover read:

OAKLAND STOCK FARM

Season 1899

Announcement and Pedigrees of the Thoroughbred Stal-
lions, CHANT (Kentucky Derby), CHEVERTON
(Oakwood Handicap). Oakland Farm, Three Miles
Northwest of Chandler, Okla. Wm. Tilghman, Owner.
Address all communications to Tom Avery, Chandler,
Okla.

Chandler's most sanguine civic boosters failed to foresee
the enormous success of the Oakland Stock Farm. It became a magnet that drew people from miles around. Political
and fraternal organizations held picnics on the grounds,
watched the quarter horses race on the farm's track, attended cock fights in the farm's pit, introduced their children to the legendary Tilghman.

Every day was like a fair, and through all the excitement

and confusion Tilghman moved with quiet dignity, his white, uncreased ten-gallon hat marking his progress. He liked the crowds and the action. He became a joiner, perhaps making up for the lonely years on the trail. He joined three fraternal lodges, because the State Marshal of the Anti-Horse Thief Association, was a delegate to the Oklahoma convention that in 1907 elected the newly admitted State's first governor, Charles N. Haskell. He was a delegate to the Democratic State Convention where he campaigned for William Jennings Bryan. He was honorary Vice-President of the Oklahoma State Fair, an official of the Jefferson Day banquets throughout the state.

One evening, while going over the farm records together, Tom Avery said, "Bill, you gonna run for office?"

Tilghman said, "What makes you ask that question?"

"I dunno, it just seems to be in the air."

"Well, Tom, I have been giving it some thought."

"I hope you decide to do it. You'd have no trouble getting elected, and you'd be a damn good governor."

"Whoa there, I'm not talking about the governorship. I plan to run for county sheriff."

Tom looked at him in amazement. "Only for sheriff?"

"It's an honorable job," Tilghman grinned.

"Sure, but . . ."

"I know how to be a sheriff—I don't know how to be a governor."

"Hell's fire, Bill! Seems to me there ain't nobody knows how to be a governor until they become one."

"Tom, I don't want to be governor! I don't want to sit in the Statehouse and have thousands of people stare at me all day, every day. I want to ride alone." He stared at the ground for a moment, kicked a pebble, then glanced sideways at Avery and grinned. "A sheriff or a marshal has a good deal of privacy, especially when it's time to arrest an outlaw. When it's time to pull a gun, you'd be surprised how much privacy the town gives you."

Tilghman was elected Lincoln County sheriff in 1900,

and re-elected by a record majority in 1902. On July 15, 1903, in the middle of his second term, he married twenty-three-year-old Zoe Agnes Stratton, the young daughter of a friend. Mayo E. Stratton was of much the same mold as his son-in-law. As a young cowhand he had driven cattle up the old Chisholm Trail, spending long hours in the saddle, fighting rain and snow and scorching drought, and the cantankerousness of the animals. He had settled in Payne County, next to Lincoln, and through hard work and shrewd trading built a prosperous ranch of several hundred head of cattle. Also like Tilghman, he raised thoroughbred horses.

Based on their common interests and problems, the two men became friends and frequently visited each other. Tilghman became very much aware of the daughter Zoe, finding her not quite like any other girl he had ever known. Just turned twenty, she was as slight as a young boy and her square face held wide-set eyes that contained great curiosity and a touch of defiance. She was not going to be patronized by anyone just because she was a girl, not even by the illustrious William Tilghman.

The fact was that Tilghman had not the slightest urge to patronize her; on the contrary, he was full of surprised admiration. She rode with her father and the cowhands, cutting out the calves, roping and branding them with skill and courage. She could discuss bloodlines with the most knowledgeable breeders. Late at night, huddled close to a kerosene lamp at her bedside, she wrote poetry. When nineteen years old she insisted on going to the newly established (1890) University of Oklahoma at Norman—and she went. It was not the frontier custom to send female children to college, but no one was really surprised when Zoe Stratton went. A neighbor said, "When she puts her mind to somethin', it gets done."

Part of the sheriff's job was to deliver mental cases to the state insane asylum at Norman, the same town where the university was located. On such trips Tilghman always looked in on Zoe so he could make a report to her father about her health and progress. Soon the two of them were corresponding, and when she came home for Christmas vacation in the year of 1902, Tilghman proposed to her. He reminded her that he had three children at home—twenty-one-year-old Dorothy, sixteen-year-old Bill, Jr., and thirteen-year-old Vonia—that he had to be away a good deal of the time and, all in all, the job he was asking her to take on was not an easy one.

"I'm not looking for something easy," she said. Then she kissed him soberly and said she would marry him the following summer.

The job was, indeed, not easy. After a brief Kansas City honeymoon, Zoe moved into the house where her stepchildren had a strong attachment to Laura Witherman, the housekeeper and surrogate mother. She wisely did not try to break up this relationship, though it left her in the equivocal position of being neither mother nor friend, merely their father's wife. She was to have three sons of her own, named Tench, Richard and Woodrow, but the age differences between the half brothers and sisters prevented intimacy. What held the family together was pride, pride in the father. Bill Tilghman was the most influential man in the county and was daily called upon for advice on everything from family quarrels to business ethics.

His fame extended far beyond Oklahoma, even to the White House. As United States Marshal he had made a number of visits to Washington where President Theodore Roosevelt always insisted that he drop into the White House and swap stories about the West. The President called him Bill and found his stories "bully."

It was not every boy and girl whose father was a successful rancher, a peace officer, and an intimate of the great. The Tilghman children were aware of their specialness.

24

In the fall of 1904, after two terms as sheriff, Tilghman announced he would not run again. His real estate and livestock holdings required his full attention, he felt, and he was fifty years old. He had done his share; let the younger men chase the outlaws.

The family was delighted at the prospect of having a full-time husband and father, but it was short-lived. Two and a half months after his term as sheriff ended, he received a large envelope containing a variety of very official looking documents, including a passport, a letter to Powell Clayton, United States Minister to Mexico, and a letter to the Mexican President, Porfirio Díaz.

That night at dinner Tilghman told his family that he would be traveling to Mexico. "The paymaster of the 'Frisco' railroad absconded with several thousand dollars and is hiding out some place in Mexico. They've asked me to find him and bring him back."

"I thought you were going to let the younger men do the work," Zoe said.

From the big envelope Tilghman removed a piece of paper and, not without pride, passed it around the table for all to see. It was White House stationery and on it were the words that made Tilghman a "special representative of Theodore Roosevelt, President of the United States."

"When the President asks you to do something, you try to do it."

The primitive train, clinging precariously to the mountainsides, required six days to travel from the Texas border to Mexico City. During the long journey Tilghman tried to lay out a campaign, but it was difficult to do because of the meager information. He had a general description of the man, he knew the name was Fitzpatrick, and that he was presumed to be some place in Mexico—a large country. The only way to proceed was to make certain assumptions based on what was known of the man's character and habits.

Fitzpatrick was, above all else, methodical. He was never late for work, never varied the route between rooming house and railway office, never left his desk in the evening without tidying it up. He showed up at the same saloon each evening, drank exactly two whiskeys, and was in bed by ten o'clock.

Not being an idler, the chances were that he would get a job. Since he knew nothing but railroading, it would be with a Mexican railroad. Tilghman considered it unlikely that Fitzpatrick would work on the main tourist line coming south from the United States, but on some obscure spur far inland. Discreet inquiries revealed that none of the crew on the main line knew Fitzpatrick, which served to confirm his theory, at least to some degree.

Upon arriving in Mexico City's terminal he secured a map of the sprawling railroad network and studied it. There was a variety of distant sections that Fitzpatrick might have chosen, but which? There was nothing to do but question the various train crews as they arrived in the capital. He was glad that he had learned the rudiments of Spanish when a young man.

The Mexican people were not to be hurried, either into work or confidences, and Tilghman forced casualness upon himself. He lolled around the station, attended the cafe where the railroad crews ate, talked about ranching and crops and sightseeing—anything but what was on his mind. After a few days he was accepted as "not a bad gringo," and his questions became more probing. He showed a photograph of Fitzpatrick, but no one knew the Americano.

He kept doggedly at it, holding to his theory simply because he had no other one to supplant it. Then he hit a lead. A porter on a provincial train coming out of the West knew of such a man as Tilghman described. He had recently come from the United States and was a conductor on a train running out of Aguascalientes, a town about three hundred miles northwest of Mexico City.

"*Gracias,*" Tilghman said, placing a silver dollar in the porter's hand. "Please do not tell anyone I was asking."

"My lips are sealed, señor. *Gracias, gracias.*"

Tilghman now made a call on the United States Minister, Powell Clayton, and reported what progress he had made. "I'd like to get these extradition papers validated today so I can catch the evening train for Aguascalientes," he said.

"We'll present them to President Díaz as soon as an audience can be arranged. It may take several days."

"I'd rather not wait for an audience with the President."

"You must wait, Mr. Tilghman. You are a personal emissary of the President of the United States. Díaz would be offended if he did not have an opportunity to pay his respects to you, and through you to President Roosevelt."

"Things are not done easily in Mexico," Tilghman observed.

"Well," said the Minister, "things are not done *quickly* in Mexico."

Three days later Tilghman and Clayton entered an elegant carriage with the seal of the United States on each side, and headed for Díaz's residence, the fortress castle of Chapultepec. Upon arrival they were greeted by a colonel caparisoned with medals and gold braid, and led to the President's office.

José de la Cruz Porfirio Díaz came from behind his desk

to shake hands with Clayton and then with Tilghman. To
Tilghman he said, "It is an honor and a pleasure to take
the hand of an emissary from my great friend, President
Roosevelt."

He was an impressive man who, though seventy-five years
old, moved with grace and power. His parents had been
Spanish but with a line of Indian blood that had broadened
his face and given his skin a touch of copper. As a young
man he had studied for the priesthood, given that up to
study law, but neither of these had left any mark on him;
he was unmistakably a general. And a dictator.

A hero because of his leadership in Mexico's 1863 war
of independence against the French and Maximilian, Díaz
had been elected President and nobody had been able to
unseat him since. His manners were impeccable, he smiled
easily, but through his black eyes there shone a small, hard
beam of arrogance. It had been over twenty years since any
man had said "no" to Porfirio Díaz.

"Your Excellency," Tilghman said, "I have this paper re-
questing the extradition of a thief who . . ."

Díaz waved his hand. "It does not matter, details do not
matter. If the great President of the United States makes
a request of Díaz, it is done."

He signed the extradition paper with a flourish, then
turning to the officer who had escorted the Americans to
his presence, he said, "Colonel Alguierrez, supply Señor
Tilghman with any number of Rurales" (national police)
"he may require to assist him. Let no wish of his go unfulfilled."

The leave-taking was another ceremony of handshakes
and bows and elaborate language. In the antechamber Colonel Alguierrez said, "I will direct the chief of the Rurales
to call upon you this afternoon and place himself under
your command."

"It's very kind of you," Tilghman said, "but I require no
assistance."

The colonel looked puzzled. "Just what are you saying, señor?"

"I will arrest him alone."

"But did you not say that he is in Aguascalientes?"

"I *think* he is there. I will go there alone and find out."

"But that is impossible, señor. That area is full of criminals. Your life would be in danger."

"Perhaps," Tilghman agreed. "On the other hand, if I arrived with a company of Rurales, everyone in a hundred miles would know of our presence and I would never find my man."

The colonel turned to the American Minister and spoke as one reasonable man to another. "Excellency, it would be most unfortunate if anything should happen to a personal representative of the great President of the United States."

"I quite agree," Clayton said. Then, to Tilghman, "If you were to be killed there could be grave international consequences."

"I'll do my best to avoid such an event," Tilghman smiled.

"I strongly recommend . . ."

"Mr. Clayton, the President has given me full authority to conduct the search and arrest in my own manner. If you are in doubt about the truth of that statement, you are at liberty to wire the White House."

"Of course not," Clayton said quickly. "It is your party, Mr. Tilghman."

The colonel took the American Minister to one side and said in a low voice, "Excellency, could you give me a paper stating that Señor Tilghman has refused to accept my offer of the Rurales? It would be most helpful to me, just in case . . ."

"Of course, of course," the Minister said. "I understand perfectly."

Aguascalientes seemed a typical Mexican town—a cluster of one- and two-story sun-baked adobe houses drowsing in the middle of a lavender plain. This first impression was deceptive, however, for the presence of a natural hot spring attracted arthritics from miles around. This flow of health seekers into town provided Tilghman with good cover; he could pose as having come for the baths (just as at Eureka Springs eight years before).

He conducted himself like any other tourist. He hired a burro and a guide to go out into the maguey fields and watch the peasants extract pulque (the white milk of cactus) which would be distilled into the lethal national drink, tequila.

Back in town he toured the shops and stalls to purchase presents for his family—hand-tooled leather purses and wallets, Mexican silver earrings and necklaces, gaily embroidered blouses. And all the time he watched and listened, and met each arriving train. On the fourth day he saw Fitzpatrick, wearing the uniform of a conductor, swing down from the steps of an incoming train. Fitzpatrick paused on the platform to run his eyes quickly over the train shed, all his nerve endings searching for danger. Seeing none, he descended to the floor and walked quickly toward an exit.

Before reaching it, a friend hailed him and began a conversation. Fitzpatrick led the friend to one side where he leaned his back against the wall and viewed the room over the friend's shoulder. He saw Tilghman casually reading a paper by the newsstand, but had no reason to mark him out of the hundred other men and women present. Tilghman had long ago learned a secret of successful surveillance and tailing—never look directly at the quarry, always look at something else and observe the man's movements with peripheral vision.

Having finished his conversation, Fitzpatrick walked quickly out of the station and down the street to enter a small grocery. Minutes later he came out with six bottles of *cerveza negra* (dark beer) and continued on to his rooming house. From across and down the street, Tilghman observed him appear in a second-floor window and reach out to close the shutters against the midday sun.

How long does it take a man to drink a bottle of beer? And how many does a lonely and guilty man drink on a hot afternoon in an alien town? Tilghman decided to allow one hour for enough beer to be consumed to slow the reflexes, befuddle the mind.

Sixty minutes later he lightly climbed the stone steps to the second floor where he studied the door to Fitzpatrick's room. It was undoubtedly bolted on the inside but the hinges seemed flimsy enough. He raised a boot and kicked.

When the door shattered, Fitzpatrick had a bottle of beer raised halfway to his lips. He held it there, looking over it into a gun barrel topped by a pair of hard blue eyes. "You're under arrest," came the words that he had known he would hear sooner or later. He glanced toward the dresser where his gun lay.

"Don't try it," Tilghman said.

Slowly he put his beer down on the floor, then extended his hands for the steel cuffs.

"There's a train out of here in thirty minutes," Tilghman said. "Drape your coat over the cuffs so they won't show. And let's go."

Back in the white, hot street, Tilghman led his prisoner at a rapid pace, studying every doorway and alley as he approached it. A thrown knife could do the job in deadly silence.

Not until they were seated in the train and it had pulled out of the station did Tilghman breathe easily. Fitzpatrick said, "I had a lot of friends back in that town. You were lucky."

"No, it is you who is unlucky," Tilghman said.

Upon his return home Tilghman was welcomed by such newspaper headlines as:

TILGHMAN GETS HIS MAN AGAIN

NO HIDING FROM TILGHMAN

OUR BILL—WELL DONE

PRESIDENT ROOSEVELT SAYS "BULLY"

Tilghman was invited to the White House to give a personal report to Theodore Roosevelt. The President was a great audience, bouncing around in his chair with excitement as Tilghman told the details of the trip.

When the story was ended, the President looked at Tilghman quizzically and said, "Bill, you've been a frontier lawman practically all your life, and you're still alive and healthy. How do you account for that fact?"

"I guess it was luck," Tilghman said.

The President waved his hand. "No, no, no! I don't believe that. Life isn't that way. They tell me you're the fastest draw and the best shot in the West. Now surely, those skills are more important than luck."

"True," Tilghman admitted.

"And yet, they wouldn't help if you were bushwhacked. There must be something else."

"Well, sir," Tilghman said thoughtfully, "when you've got the right on your side you've always got an edge on the other man."

The President slapped the palm of his hand on the desk and cried, "Bully!"

Before he left the White House it was made clear to Tilghman that he could have any of a number of jobs at the President's disposal. He wanted none. By now he was rich in land and stock, rich in progeny, and rich in honors. He had only one unfulfilled ambition: to see statehood given to the land he loved.

When on November 16, 1907, Congress proclaimed Oklahoma a State, Tilghman was content. His days of danger were surely ended.

25

Many Oklahomans, including Tilghman, thought that state-hood would solve all their problems. It was, therefore, with disbelief that they heard in the spring of 1909 that the Creeks were again on the warpath. The tribal leader was Chitto Harjo, meaning Crazy Snake. "Snake" was his tribal name, "Crazy" meant recklessly brave.

Food was what had sparked the fire between red and white men—just as it had back in the time of the buffalo. The Creeks were said to have raided a white man's smoke-house and made off with sides of beef and lamb. Three deputy sheriffs went to the Creek camp to arrest Chitto Harjo but the Indians resisted and in the gunfight that followed two of the deputies were killed. The nearby town of Henryetta exploded in rage and a posse set out to punish the Indians. Chitto Harjo had led his people to the hills and all the posse found was an Indian Christian preacher driving a horse and buggy. They killed him.

Two companies of the newly established Oklahoma militia, under the command of Colonel Roy V. Hoffman, were dispatched to Henryetta where they encamped a few miles out of town. They made numerous forays into the rocky hills but found no trace of the Creeks.

Soon after, Tilghman received a telegram from Governor

Charles N. Haskell asking him to come to the capitol. After
reading the message aloud to Zoe, he folded the paper and
put it in his pocket.

"What does the governor want with you?" Zoe asked.

"He doesn't say."

"Might be about that trouble with the Creeks over Henryetta way?"

"I suppose it is."

"You knew Crazy Snake?"

Tilghman nodded. "Must be in his sixties but he's as
straight and strong as a young brave. He's old-fashioned
and wants his people to keep their culture and customs."

"He's living in the wrong age, seems to me."

"I suppose he is," Bill nodded glumly. "I saw Crazy Snake
shortly after the homesteaders began to move in on him, and
he said, 'I wouldn't mind playing the white man's game if
only the white man didn't make all the rules.'"

"You can't stop progress, Bill."

"Of course, of course. The country has to grow, but we
sure pay a price."

That evening Tilghman caught the train out of Chandler
and the next morning sat with Governor Haskell.

"Bill, I want you to find Crazy Snake. The militia is cost-
ing the state fifteen hundred dollars a day and they haven't
turned up a clue."

"He's probably not near Henryetta, Governor."

"That's the trouble, he's taken to the hills where nobody
could find him but you, Bill. You look reluctant."

"I suppose I am, Governor."

"Let me remind you that my home is in Muskogee, the
heart of the Creek country. I know those Indians and I
like them, but that does not release me from enforcing
the law. Suppose those deputies had been shot in a white
village: Wouldn't we have tried to arrest the man who
pulled the trigger? Do we ignore the law just because Indians are involved?"

"You're right, of course," Tilghman said. "I'll go get Crazy Snake."

For four weeks Tilghman was on the trail going from cabin to cabin, camp to camp, but he found no trace of Crazy Snake. The proud old man had escaped. Some said he went to Mexico. In any event he was never again seen in Oklahoma. Without their leader, the tribe was soon "pacified."

When Bill returned home *without* his man, an almost perfect arrest record was broken. People close to him reported that he didn't seem to mind.

Squire Tilghman had replaced Marshal Tilghman. He became president of the Chandler town council (equivalent of mayor), a State Senator, Theodore Roosevelt's special guest at the inauguration of William Howard Taft as President of the United States on March 4, 1909. His advice and council were sought by many men on many subjects. When the merchants of Oklahoma City began a campaign to make their town pre-eminent on the entire prairie, they consulted Tilghman.

Henry Overholser and his committee of civic boosters had been behind the campaign to make Oklahoma City the State Capital. Now they came up with a new project: the staging of an annual State Fair. And who knew most about fairs? Bill Tilghman. He had produced an outstanding county fair in his home town of Chandler, and on the basis of that success had been summoned by many towns to assist in similar ventures. The central attraction in all the fairs was the horse races, and certainly few men knew more about breeding and racing than Bill Tilghman.

Under Tilghman's general supervision the Oklahoma State Fair became a place of "wonderment, education and thrills." There was a large hall for the ladies' farm exhibits and competitions, canned fruit, baked bread, fancy crochet work, patchwork quilts, and smocking. Another building held the livestock show where blue ribbons waited the best cow, bull, ram, pig and chicken. There were minstrel shows

and monkey shows, a glass-blowing exhibit. There were
horse pulling contests, shooting matches, balloon ascensions,
a sideshow titled *Paris by Night.*

The highlight of the fair was the horse races that took
place on the newly graded oval track flanked by grand-
stands that could seat 2000 people! Tilghman raced his
horses there, and for those races which he did not enter, he
was a judge. The Oklahoma State Fair races became the
most important and profitable of all the races in the western
circuit.

Oklahoma City had always been a wide-open town in
the frontier tradition but with the coming of statehood,
and her designation as State Capital, she felt the need for
respectability. On May 9, 1911, a citizens' reform movement
elected businessman Whit M. Grant as mayor and he in
turn announced his intention of getting the "best man possible" to head the police department. Everyone knew that
the "best man" was Bill Tilghman, but there were doubts
that he could be persuaded to take on such a difficult and
thankless job.

Prior to Election Day, Grant and Tilghman had had a
frank talk. "Bill, you'll be boss of the department. I won't
interfere as long as you wear the badge."

"You in favor of enforcing *all* the laws?" Tilghman asked.
The state had recently voted itself dry.

"*All* laws," Grant said, "including the dry law. I don't
approve of prohibition, but as long as it's the law it should
be enforced." He gave Tilghman a grin. "Besides, strict enforcement ought to be a good way to get it repealed."

"You say the police force is full of grafters?"

"I don't have chapter and page but it's common knowledge that most of our policemen are for sale."

"It's been my experience that 'common knowledge' is often no knowledge at all. It's a poor way to judge a man."

"I leave that up to you, Bill. Find the bad apples and
pitch them out. I'll stand behind you."

Tilghman pulled thoughtfully on his graying mustache.

"It's my belief that few policemen, sheriffs or marshals want to be bribed. When it does happen it's mainly because they've lost pride in their job and, therefore, pride in themselves. If the top command is honest and just, you don't generally have to worry about the lower ranks."

"You can fire every lieutenant and captain and inspector on the force if you think it necessary. I can't put it in stronger terms, Bill—you will be the boss!"

Tilghman nodded, not in acceptance but in approval of the arrangements.

"Will you take the job, Bill? Will you help me make Oklahoma City a decent town?"

"I'm inclined to join you, Whit, but I'll have to discuss it with my wife."

"I understand, Bill, but I'd appreciate it if you'd let me know your decision at the earliest possible moment."

"You want to announce it before Election Day," Bill grinned.

"You're damn right I do!"

"I'll let you know this weekend."

Zoe could see he was preoccupied when he came home late that day. He never kept anything from her, good news or bad, but he took his own time in breaking it. It wasn't until after supper and the children had been put to bed that he broached the subject.

"Zoe, how would you like to move to Oklahoma City for a time?"

"Why, I don't know, Bill. Why do you want to move?"

"They want me to be chief of police."

"Oh?" she gave him a mocking smile.

"I know I promised to give up police work but they need me to reorganize the force. Two years is all I'll give it. That's what I told them and what I promise you. Two years and we'll come back to Chandler."

"I'll keep you to that promise," she said soberly.

26

The land on which Oklahoma City was being built, the vast grass-sweet prairie, had been fought over and bled over for decades: white man versus red man, homesteader versus rancher, closed town versus open town, wets versus drys.

Tilghman took with him to Oklahoma City the conviction that the policeman should be above these quarrels—at least while on his beat. When on his own time and out of uniform, he was free to denounce Carry Nation or Samuel Gompers or President Taft or anybody else—but not on the job.

He had a few other strongly held principles which he explained to his men in a series of meetings at Police Headquarters. "First off, I want to tell you men that I will have no 'confidential squad' to spy on you and report back to me. I will not listen to tales of police misconduct that happened before my arrival. I'm interested only in the now and the future. At this moment I consider every one of you to be a trustworthy officer, and I will hold that opinion until you force me to change it. A final word: You don't have to make a lot of arrests to prove yourselves to me. Some of the best men I've known made very few arrests, they kept their beats orderly and quiet *without* arresting people.

Let your very presence on the street be a warning to the criminal, a reassurance to the innocent. That's all I have to say, men. Dismissed."

The men applauded and cheered him. His simple, straightforward speech gave a great boost to the department's morale, and the patrolmen walked their beats with new pride, new security. They were not afraid to make an arrest, and they were not afraid not to make an arrest. They knew that the man behind the big desk at headquarters understood their problems.

There was also a honeymoon between Tilghman and the citizens. They were proud to have the most famous marshal in the Territories as their chief; it fit in with their vision of Oklahoma City's becoming the biggest and the best city on the plains. People felt a new security by simply watching Tilghman's grandfatherly figure walk the streets with stately step.

All this mutual good will was not to last long, however. Ten days after taking the job Tilghman ordered the arrest of twelve known bootleggers, and the town exploded.

A worried friend came to Tilghman's office to report, "Bill, you've offended a lot of people."

"Every arrest offends somebody," Tilghman observed.

"Quite true, Bill, but in this case you've outraged the bootleggers' customers, and that's just about everybody in town."

"What would you have me do?"

"Well, I don't rightly know," his friend admitted, "but at least you can make a statement to the press. Call in the reporters and give them your side of the story."

The following day Chief Tilghman received the reporters in his office. They started to question him, but he cut them off. "Gentlemen, I will make a statement and you may quote me: My job, as I see it, is to enforce all the laws on the books—not just the laws I approve of, but *all* of them. If the people of Oklahoma City don't like their town dry, they can vote it wet. Until they do, however, I'll enforce the law as now written. It's as simple as that. That is all I have to say."

And it *was* simple as that. The citizens saw the logic in Tilghman's statement and muted their criticism, but they did not change the law. With human contradiction they wanted both prohibition and booze. Tilghman's drive against bootleggers did not dry up the town, it only made liquor more difficult to obtain and, therefore, more expensive. And the citizens didn't like that. They said to each other that Tilghman was a fine man, no doubt about that, but they wished he'd be "reasonable."

Now a new problem appeared—union organizers came to town. They were denounced in the press as "anarchists." There was a widespread demand that the police arrest them and ship them out of town. Tilghman replied, "If they violate the law, I will arrest them." This did not seem to satisfy anyone and there was talk of tar and feathers for the union men.

A large restaurant in midtown was the first business to be picketed and through that morning tempers became inflamed on both sides. During the noon rush hour one of the pickets attacked a diner who refused to honor the line. Tilghman arrested the picket at once.

Within the hour the union organizer was pounding Tilghman's desk and warning of his high political connections in Washington, D.C. Tilghman heard him out, then said, "The problem is a simple one, sir. We have a law against disturbing the peace, and your man violated that law. Every time one of your men starts a fight he'll be arrested. If you conduct a peaceful line I'll protect you."

The organizer sneered, "Don't try to con me, mister. You want me to believe that if one of the local big shots lays one on the chin of a picket, you'll arrest *him?*"

"That's exactly what I mean. I'll arrest anybody who disturbs the peace."

To his amazement, the organizer found himself believing the Chief of Police. *That* had never happened to him before. As he turned to go, Tilghman stopped him with a question.

"Son, can I give you some advice?"

"Yes, sir."

"Don't put any contentious men on the line, men who are looking for trouble. They'll be sure to find it."

From that day the picket line was peaceful, but that was not what the local merchants really wanted. Among themselves they admitted Tilghman was enforcing the letter of the law, but insisted he was violating the *spirit* of the law. What the law really meant, they said, was that the radicals should be driven out of town. Tilghman's trouble was that he simply wasn't "flexible."

Tilghman had his supporters, including Mayor Grant, but the unblinkable fact was that month by month he was losing public support. "It's nothing personal," Tilghman observed philosophically one evening to his friend, John Hale, who had stopped in at Police Headquarters. "We've got to remember that a good three-quarters of the people here have never before lived in a city. They've been ranchers and farmers and prospectors, men who lived alone and without tether. Suddenly they find themselves jammed together with thousands of other people and they can no longer do exactly as they like, other people have rights too. Pretty soon they'll understand."

"Education like that comes slow, Bill, and in the meantime the newspaper is trying to cut you in ribbons."

Tilghman ruefully rubbed the back of his neck. "That's something else. I'm not sure what goes on there."

The editor-owner of the local newspaper had declared war on Tilghman. No, actually there had been no open declaration, it was a subtle campaign of character assassination. All the news stories that touched on crime or police matters were carefully slanted against Tilghman. By quoting out of context, by printing half-truths, the Chief of Police was made to appear stupid or venal, or both.

"You should fight back," Hale declared.

"How?"

"By issuing denials."

"And who would print the denials? Our friend the editor? Can you imagine how he'd twist or distort anything I might say? Every time I speak in public I give him a new opportunity to attack, so the best thing for me is to keep quiet and do my job the best I can."

"It's not fair, damn it!"

"No, I suppose it isn't. But I've discovered that life is frequently unfair. Perhaps it's the Almighty's way of testing us."

A sergeant opened the office door and said in a low voice, "Mr. Fowler is here again, Chief."

A grin appeared on Tilghman's face and he said to Hale, "Our editor has his enemies—Mr. Fowler is one of them. He stops by here once a week with new plans for revenge. Send him in, Sergeant."

Mr. Fowler was short and round and had a pink, bald head which he frequently wiped with an enormous handkerchief. His small, wet eyes looked questioningly toward Hale. Tilghman introduced them and said that Fowler could speak in Hale's presence.

"I've got him, I've got him!" Fowler exclaimed. "I've been tailing the sonofabitch for a month, and now I've got him."

"Just where have you got him, Mr. Fowler?" Tilghman asked.

"In the Excelsior Hotel. He's in room 214 with a woman. He just took her up there five minutes ago. You've got plenty of time to raid the hotel, Chief. I'll go back and stake out the place, just in case he tries to escape out the back way when your men arrive."

With a broad wink, the happy conspirator disappeared through the door. Tilghman made a steeple of his fingers and rested his chin upon them.

After some moments John Hale said, "You're not going to do it?"

"No, John, I'm not."

"Damn it, after all his attacks on you, do you think he deserves any consideration?"

"Oh, I wasn't thinking about him. I was thinking about his wife and daughter. They would be the ones to suffer most. I just can't do it to them."

"You could do it without their knowing. Arrest him and the girl, but don't book them. Just warn him that . . ."

"Oh, you mean blackmail?"

"Well . . ."

"Do you find the word hard to say, John? Well, I'd find it hard to do."

Hale tried another tack. "As I recall it, when you took this job you swore to enforce all laws all the time, no matter who might be involved."

"Did I say that?" Then, with a pixyish grin, "You see how wrong my critics are? I can be flexible after all."

The owner of the paper continued to print attacks on Tilghman; neither he nor his wife and daughter ever knew what they had been spared.

One evening, after she had put her sons to bed, Zoe Tilghman said to her husband, "Bill, the two years are about up."

He lowered the newspaper. "What two years?"

"The two years you've been chief."

"They can't be!"

"We came here in July 1911. This is 1913. Remember your promise to serve only two years?"

"Yes, I remember. But I hate to leave an unfinished job."

"Bill, it will never be finished!"

"Yes, I guess you're right."

"You told me that all categories of crime have gone down this past year. That's record enough. You can't make crime disappear."

"I am tired, Zoe."

"So am I. Let's go home."

27

There was only one job that Tilghman wanted and failed to receive—Chief United States Marshal for the State of Oklahoma. He wanted to succeed Evett Nix. He had been promised the job, but in the swirl of national politics the appointment never came from Washington. If he had asked for it during Teddy Roosevelt's terms as President, it would have been his, but by the time he got around to announcing his ambition William Howard Taft was in the White House. Also, Tilghman was a Democrat in a predominantly Republican state. There was some irony in the fact that the job for which he was best suited was never his.

He was neither mournful nor bitter; he hardly had time. Projects, alarms and excursions were constantly being brought to him at Chandler.

Fred Sutton was a frequent visitor at the Tilghman ranch, and on a spring afternoon shortly after Tilghman had returned from Oklahoma City, he arrived with a preoccupied air. For a time the two old friends rocked on the front porch and silently admired the livestock grazing nearby. Sutton broke the silence.

"You've heard what's going on in Mexico, Bill?"

"The assassination of Madero? I've heard."

The old dictator, José de la Cruz Porfirio Díaz, had been

toppled and exiled in the spring of 1911, his place taken by Francesco Madero. Now, in the spring of 1913, another revolution, led by Victoriano Huerta, had imprisoned and murdered Madero.

"The fact is," Sutton said, "Mexico seems to be coming apart and we've got to do something to protect our investments down there."

"What do you propose to do, Fred?"

"I'm organizing a company of Oklahoma Sharp Shooters, along the lines of Teddy Roosevelt's Rough Riders, and we'll go down there and occupy the mines and oil wells that damn well belong to us. I've recruited thirty-nine men so far. Here, look at the list, Bill."

Scrawled on a long sheet of legal paper were the names of men ready to shoulder arms and march south. There were police officers, city commissioners, judges and businessmen. Bill knew them all.

"Fred, are you serious about this?" Tilghman asked.

"Dead serious. And we want you to lead us. By unanimous vote we ask you to lead us."

Tilghman was incredulous. "Lead you against what? You want me to just blindly lead a handful of men over the border without knowing what waits us?"

"We know in general the situation at Matamoras—it's occupied by a counter-counterrevolutionary army led by a General Blanco."

"How many men does he command?"

"A couple of thousand rag-tail troops. One American is worth a dozen Mexicans."

Tilghman became impatient. "If we're shot we bleed, just like a Mexican. If we march down there the battle will be won, not by the smartest or even the bravest, but by the side that has the greatest fire power."

Sutton was crestfallen. "I warned the boys you'd take this attitude, and I suppose you're right. Bill, will you go down there and just investigate the situation? We'll pay expenses and whatever fee you want."

At the end of the month Tilghman rode south to Browns-
ville, Texas, and there crossed the border to disappear into
Mexico. Some concern was felt for his safety. Yankees were
not very popular in Mexico this year, especially Yankees who
asked military questions. It was a great relief when his first
report arrived by mail. It read:

"I had a long talk with General Blanco. He is a very in-
telligent man, and I would judge him to be a good man. His
army is a poverty-stricken looking bunch. They are poorly
equipped for war. Their horses are poor, and consist of a
very poor class of mustang ponies. If it came to a fight, they
could not make much of a battle with the arms they have,
and they could not make a decent retreat with their mounts.

"Blanco says he is battling for the rights of his people,
and could soon whip the Federalistas if he were permitted
to transport arms and munitions from the United States . . .

"Bill Murray[1] said in a speech in Oklahoma City the
night before I left that he and the President[2] had different
views in regard to the Mexican situation. That he was in
favor of intervention; that if he had the power to do so, he
would surround the border with the U. S. Army, take charge
of all the customs houses; send our war vessels to the coast
and capture all the customs houses there; then march into
the interior with our soldiers and take the city of Mexico.
And in thirty days the troubles in Mexico would be ended,
probably without a shot fired.

"He failed to tell the people what he would do with the
ten million paupers in Mexico, most of whom never looked
in a book or had a shoe on their feet; and the outlaw bands
in the mountains that we could not subdue with all the U. S.
Army for years to come."

The report not only cooled the ardor of Sutton's "Oklahoma Sharp Shooters," but echoes of it carried all the way
to Washington, D.C., where it influenced the debate going
on in Congress. The report made a great impact because of
the author's total objectivity. He had set out to prove no

[1] "Alfalfa Bill" Murray, a future Governor of Oklahoma
[2] Woodrow Wilson

thesis, to buttress no prejudices; he simply reported what he saw with a trained eye. If the report made it unwise to invade Mexico, this conclusion had been reached by facts, not by rhetoric.

Three years later American troops did invade Mexico, but under somewhat different circumstances. Bandit-revolutionary Pancho Villa had been making forays into Texas, and Brigadier General John J. Pershing led an expeditionary force to pursue and punish him. The United States never did attempt to occupy and annex Mexico as Sutton had proposed.

Telegrams were becoming commonplace, especially at the Tilghman ranch, but Zoe could never quite get over the belief a message so urgent as to be sent by wire had to be bad news. On a summer day shortly after Tilghman's return from Mexico, she stood impatiently on the front porch, waiting for her husband to come in from his daily inspection of his horses. In her hand was a sealed yellow envelope. She waved it in the air when she saw Tilghman in the distance.

He dismounted beside her, received the envelope and tore it open. It read: MADSEN AND I COMING TO CHANDLER TO SEE YOU NEXT MONDAY STOP IF INCONVENIENT WIRE ANOTHER DATE STOP NIX

"Now, what would Mr. Nix want of you?" Zoe asked.

"Something about law work, I suppose."

"But he's retired as Marshal. Lives in St. Louis, you told me."

Bill grinned. "Once you got law work in your blood, it's not easy to get rid of it. And besides, Madsen is coming with him. What else could it be?"

Monday afternoon Madsen and Nix rode in to Tilghman's ranch and the old friends greeted each other with the special warmth and intimacy that exists between men who have faced danger together. Zoe served coffee, bread and jam, then discreetly withdrew.

Nix finally got to the reason for this visit. "Bill, have you seen that movie called *Beating Back?*"

"No, but I hear it's pretty bad."

"It's worse than you've heard," Nix said grimly. "If the people believe that movie tells the truth, there's apt to be a lot of bad history written in the future."

The movie Nix referred to purported to be the life story of Al Jennings, leader of the Jennings gang which had a brief career after the Doolin gang had been smashed. The gang had consisted of Al and Frank Jennings (sons of a respected judge), Pat and Morris O'Malley, and "Little Dick" West.

Never in the history of the West had there been such inept bad men as the Jennings gang. On August 18, 1897, they held up a train at Edmond, Oklahoma, but when the conductor refused to take them seriously, they turned their horses and rode away. A month later they attempted to hold up an M.K.T. train at Muskogee, Oklahoma, but the train refused to stop for them. After that they planned to rob the bank at Minco, Oklahoma, but when they arrived, they found the local sheriff leaning against the building and lost their nerve. They had a single success, or partial success. They held up a Rock Island train in the Chickasaw Territory and tried to blow open a safe in the baggage car. The car was wrecked but the safe remained locked. There was nothing left to do but rob the passengers. The loot netted each man about $40.

The United States Marshals tracked them down, killing "Little Dick" in the process. They were all sentenced to prison, Al for five years. Their outlaw career had lasted a total of fourteen weeks.

Upon receiving a pardon, Al Jennings ran for public office, became an evangelist. His life was sentimentalized in a story entitled "Beating Back" written for *The Saturday Evening Post* by journalist Will Irwin. That story became the basis for a motion picture in which the marshals were portrayed as not only stupid, but sadistic. The good guys were the outlaws, the bad guys the marshals.

Nix said to Tilghman, "Everybody thinks it's time that someone produced a movie that tells the truth about Oklahoma outlaws. I've raised the money to finance such a film and we want you to act in it and direct it, Bill."

The Eagle Film Company was organized to produce a single movie entitled *The Passing of the Oklahoma Outlaws*. It traced the bloody careers of the Doolin and Jennings gangs and Tilghman was the star as well as the director. His direction may have lacked subtilty, the cast may have acted in a wooden, self-conscious manner, but the story was absolutely authentic. It was filmed in Guthrie, on the Dunn ranch, at the dugout, and finally down at Eureka Springs. Whenever possible the marshals and outlaws played themselves. Besides Tilghman, the men who appeared before the camera included Nix, Madsen, John Hale, and the sole survivor of the Doolin gang, Arkansas Tom. He had been serving a fifty-year sentence but Tilghman had helped to arrange parole for him after serving seventeen years.

Tilghman's insistence on accuracy of every detail made for a very slow shooting schedule. They had started the film in the middle of 1914, and the following year they were still at it in the plains and caves west of Chandler.

During the last week of March 1915, Tilghman was consulting with cameraman J. B. Kent when one of his own ranch hands galloped up and shouted, "There's been a holdup in Stroud! Both banks robbed!"

"*Both* banks?" Tilghman asked.

"Both the Stroud State and the First National, at the same time."

This had not been attempted since the Dalton gang had descended on Coffeyville. "Who did it?" Bill asked.

"The Starr gang."

During the brief conversation Tilghman had been removing the blanks from his gun and replacing them with live lead bullets. Nix and Madsen had done the same thing and when Tilghman mounted and headed east for Stroud, they rode beside him.

Tilghman turned to his ranch hand and said, "How'd you hear about it?"

"Telephone call come into Chandler for you. It was from Henry Starr himself. He got wounded and caught by the townspeople. There's talk of lynchin' and he wants you to rescue him."

Nix and Madsen burst out laughing.

Henry Starr was a part Cherokee bandit who boasted that he had robbed more banks than any other man in America. He was probably right. In one five-month period, between September 8, 1914, and January 13, 1915, he and his gang robbed fourteen!

Stroud was in a lynching mood, all right; Tilghman could almost smell it when he entered the town. Small groups of men stood on street corners and spoke together in low tones. There was a hush on the town, the unnatural quiet that often precedes violence. The largest crowd was in front of the First National Bank where Dr. John Evans had his offices on the second floor. Henry Starr was there.

"Hello, Marshal," Starr said weakly as Tilghman entered the outer office where he was stretched out on a leather couch. His left leg was splinted and bandaged. His face was drained of color but he managed a wry smile. "I never thought I'd be glad to see you."

"What's his condition, Doctor?" Tilghman asked.

"I removed the bullet but the left leg is broken in several places."

"Can you get me out of here?" Starr asked Tilghman.

"Can he travel?" Tilghman asked Evans.

"Sure, but he'll have a lot of pain."

"Won't be as painful as a necktie party," Starr said. "Can you do it, Marshal?"

Tilghman turned to Lincoln County Deputy Sheriff

George Wilson with a questioning look. Wilson said, "The sooner we get him out of here, the better."

There was an angry murmur from the crowd when Starr, carried on a litter, came into view. Tilghman flipped back his coattail to give him easier access to his gun, then marched straight ahead. The crowd parted, reluctantly, but in time. The next westbound Santa Fe train was flagged down and Starr put aboard without incident.

When they were under way Tilghman pointed to the wounded leg and said, "How'd it happen, Henry?"

Starr grimaced with disgust. "All my men were riding ahead of me and were safely out of town. As I was riding past the butcher shop I got it. A seventeen-year-old kid hiding behind some salt barrels shot me with a hog gun. A *hog gun!* It's humiliating!"

When brought to trial, Starr pleaded guilty and was sentenced to twenty-five years in the Oklahoma State Penitentiary. Tilghman went back to work on his movie, concluding it with the scene of Starr being shot with a hog gun.

The Passing of the Oklahoma Outlaws was received by the public with modest enthusiasm. Newspapers pointed out the strong moral the picture taught and urged parents to take their children to see it as a sort of inoculation against a criminal career. The truth was it was an amateur production and it had to compete with pictures being made in a new town called Hollywood. The same year Tilghman's picture was completed, D. W. Griffith offered to movie fans *The Birth of a Nation.*

The only way Tilghman could fill the movie houses, he discovered, was by personal appearances. On September 1, 1915, he wrote Zoe from Denver: ". . . We are doing well at the Tabor Grand . . . My lecture is a drawing card . . . The proprietor said yesterday that he wouldn't have the picture without me. I wanted to go to Cheyenne Friday and Saturday but he wouldn't let me go . . . I talked about six hours yesterday and was completely worn out last night."

It was arduous work for a man in his sixties, but Tilghman felt a responsibility to the stockholders of the Eagle Film Company. He knew that they had invested their money in the film because of him, and it was his obligation to see that they didn't lose any of it.

Too, it was something of a triumphal tour. It was pleasant to be recognized, to be applauded, to be thanked for helping to tame the West and make it a safe place in which to live and raise a family. He was less easy in the company of celebrities who now sought him out. Sports champions, theatrical stars, and politicians would suddenly appear, throw their arms around his shoulders in the most intimate manner, and give a toothy grin, not at him but at a camera which was to record their own brave endorsement of law and order. Tilghman did not take easily to the feigned friendships, but he was assured that it was all part of "show biz," good for the box office. He endured them.

28

After the motion picture had paid off its investors and turned a good profit besides, Tilghman once more retired to his breeding farm. And once more he was summoned to the State Capital and asked to help in a crisis. It was in the fall of 1921.

Governor J. B. A. Robertson greeted him warmly and escorted him to a chair beside his desk. Robertson was a towering man who weighed 280 pounds, all of it muscle. As a young man he had been an amateur boxer, and he still moved with grace and controlled power.

"Bill," he said, "is the Ku Klux Klan strong in Lincoln County?"

"Not as strong as in Tulsa," Tilghman replied.

The governor grimaced, for the Klan had recently provoked a race riot in that city. "At least one good thing came out of Tulsa," Robertson observed. "Those who said the Klan is small and disorganized now know better. And those who said that the only aim of the Klan is 'to keep the niggers in their place' know better, too. At least half the Klan oratory in Tulsa was directed against Jews and Catholics. Oh, by the way, how do you stand on the Klan, Bill?"

"I'm against them."

"I knew you would be. But what about the others, the responsible people in Chandler?"

"The great majority are against the Klan."

"But they haven't spoken out."

"No, sir, they haven't."

"They afraid?"

"That's part of it. Also, there is prudence. They don't think their small voices can accomplish much. They're waiting for someone in high office to speak out, to give them leadership."

"Someone like the governor?"

"Yes, sir, someone like the governor."

Robertson studied the ceiling for a long moment. "The Klan has sent a request that I discharge certain officers in the State Militia. Some of my friends have advised me to play along quietly, not to stir up trouble. They think the Klan has reached its peak and will soon begin a decline if we just ignore it. What do you think?"

"I think the Klan is growing because too many people are ignoring it. If you give in to these demands you'll immediately receive new and bigger ones. The day it is known they have successfully pressured the governor, their numbers will double."

"Then, your advice is . . ."

"Tell them to go to hell."

Robertson grinned. "I like that advice." From a desk drawer he removed an official document and handed it to Tilghman to read. It was a directive to the State Militia stating that no officer could be a member of the Klan.

"I'll issue this directive tomorrow," the governor said. "It will mean a showdown with the Klan. When it happens, Bill, I'd like you to be at my side."

Tilghman nodded. "I'll be there."

After the governor's directive to the State Militia was made public there was silence. The Klan leaders did not denounce it, there were no parades, no fiery crosses burned. Some of the governor's advisers told him that his strong stand had saved the day, that the Klan was afraid to take issue with him, that he had routed them. Tilghman was not in agreement.

"The Klan has simply decided not to use this issue to fight you, Governor," he said. "They're searching for some other issue in which their position would be more popular. They'll find it soon, or they'll create one."

Prophetic words!

In the postwar depression many banks had failed throughout the nation. Now it happened to the Citizens' State Bank of Okmulgee, and 4000 depositors were penniless, frightened and angry. The hooded men had their issue.

The Klan began a whispering campaign which accused the governor and his state bank commissioner, Fred Dennis, with complicity and malfeasance. They implied that the governor had looted the bank and thus impoverished the people of Okmulgee.

Governor Robertson counterattacked by ordering the state attorney general to investigate the bank failure, but in the meantime the Klan was able to force local officials to impanel a Grand Jury to hear its charges. The struggle for power was now joined.

Tilghman made a tour of Okmulgee, quietly observing, asking questions, then he went back to Oklahoma City to report to Governor Robertson.

"It's like a town under siege," Tilghman said, "but with a difference. In the old days when the Indians threatened a village the people always knew where the enemy was—out there, across the prairie. But in Okmulgee the enemy is *inside* the village and no one knows his face. Neighbors have stopped talking to each other, out of fear and suspicion. Policemen hesitate to make arrests, they might be taking an important Klansman to jail. It's a silent war in which the majority of people are opposed to the Klan but in self-protection want to do nothing to offend the winners. But since no one is sure which side will win, few people do anything at all."

"As bad as that," Robertson muttered.

"I was there for three days and not once did I hear a man tell a joke."

The door in the governor's office opened and an aide stepped inside. "Judge Christopher is on the telephone, sir. He's calling from Guthrie, and says it's important that he speak to you."

"Put his call through," Robertson instructed, reaching for the phone on his desk.

H. R. Christopher was Judge of the Superior Court in Okmulgee. As a Roman Catholic he was a target for abuse by the Klan.

"Did you see him when you were there, Bill?" the governor asked.

"Yes, sir. A good man."

The governor spoke into the phone. "Howdy, Judge. What you doing all the way up in Guthrie?"

The governor listened for several minutes while his face turned serious, then dark. Finally he broke in on the monologue coming from the other end of the line. "So the Klan burned a cross on your lawn last night. That doesn't make you unique; they're burning crosses all over the state."

The governor listened again and then, explosively, he slammed his fist on his desk. "Damn it, Christopher, you *can't* resign! I know you're concerned for your wife and children. Send them out of town if you think it necessary, but you're a *judge!* You go back home and sit on that bench and if it becomes necessary, I'll send the State Militia to protect you."

Whatever more the judge might have had to say, it was cut off as the governor slammed the receiver down on the phone and shoved the instrument roughly away from him. He said ruefully, "Of course, I don't really have any authority to send him back."

"You certainly sounded like you did," Tilghman grinned.

"Will he go, Bill?"

"I think so. I pray so. Okmulgee is our Armageddon and the whole state is watching."

Grand Jury proceedings are, by law, secret; but not those being held in Okmulgee. Dominated by the Klan, the jury let it be known its intention to indict both the governor and Fred Dennis, state banking commissioner, for criminal conspiracy.

When news of this reached the capitol the governor immediately sent for Dennis. "Fred, things are getting nasty down at Okmulgee."

"Yes, I've heard."

"I want you to get all your records together and take them down to that Grand Jury."

"They may refuse to hear me."

"Make them hear you, damn it! Walk right through their door and *make* them look at the truth."

Robertson went out to lunch. When he returned he found on his desk the resignation of Fred Dennis. His first impulse was to storm into the man's office and berate him, but he didn't. His rage left him and he slumped heavily into his chair. He wondered: Could a man be denounced for thinking first of his wife and children? Should he be labeled a coward just because he didn't share another's vision of a proper world? Robertson didn't know the answers. But he was suddenly tired and discouraged.

He stared gloomily at the phone on his desk for fully five minutes before he was able to reach for it. By the greatest act of will he removed the receiver and said into it, "Get me Tilghman."

After several moments Tilghman's calm voice said, "Yes, Governor?"

"Bill, the time for the showdown has come. I'm going to Okmulgee tomorrow."

"All right. I'd like to make some advance security arrangements down there. I can pick you up about seven o'clock tomorrow morning, if that's all right with you."

"That will be just fine," the governor said, some of the old briskness returning to his voice.

A large crowd had gathered in front of the Okmulgee courthouse that day. They didn't know why they were there, they only knew that the Klan's Grand Cyclops for Oklahoma had told them to be there. As an hour passed, then a second one, the crowd became restive. They had expected action and they were in no mood to be denied it.

As yet unseen, but approaching the town from the west, was a small caravan of cars: a Reo, a National, a Velie and a Ford. Headed out of town west to meet the caravan was a Maxwell driven by William Crume, Tilghman's old under-sheriff at Chandler. He had been in town for the past twelve hours to observe developments. He flagged down the caravan and made his report to Tilghman and the governor in the second car.

"There's a Klan mob in front of the courthouse. The leaders told them to come there but nobody knows exactly why."

"Perhaps to block all entrance to the courthouse and the Grand Jury room," Tilghman said. "If that's true, we've got a leak somewhere in the capitol."

"By God, if . . ." the governor exploded.

Tilghman put a hand on his arm. "We can look into that later." Then to Crume, "What do you recommend?"

"That mob has been standing around for a long time and is getting in a nasty mood. Now, there's a rear entrance to the courthouse, a basement service entrance that's kept locked. I have the key to it and we can get the governor into the building before the mob knows he's in town."

Tilghman turned to Robertson. "What do you say, Governor?"

"Bill, I told you that you can run this show the way you see fit."

"Well," said Tilghman, "we came here for a test of strength. Smuggling the governor in the back door doesn't seem to do that."

"I agree!" the governor boomed.

"I propose we drive right through the crowd and up to the front door. We'll have the advantage of surprise."

"Let's go," said the governor.

Twenty minutes later the crowd observed the motor caravan coming down the street; it slowly made way as the cars moved through them and halted at the courthouse steps. Out of the second car stepped Bill Tilghman and a sound like a sigh went through the crowd. They all knew Tilghman, knew him as an enemy, and his appearance here meant something really big was about to happen. Next out of the car was Governor Robertson and now the crowd was truly surprised, and excited. Quickly the passengers in the other cars climbed out and among them were Chris Madsen, Baird H. Markham (Oklahoma Adjutant General) and Major A. Herskowitz (an officer in the National Guard).

Tilghman led the way through the crowd and up the steps. He shoved men aside with a casual sort of hauteur, acting as if he were barely aware of their existence. The governor's party had disappeared into the building before the crowd recovered from surprise sufficiently to boo. When the sound came it was ragged and ugly—an animal sound.

The county attorney's office was on the second floor and when they arrived at it Robertson said to his escorting party, "You wait out here. I want to talk to him alone." He turned and entered the office, shutting the door behind him.

Soon after, loud and angry voices issued from the office. "Think maybe we'd better go in there?" Major Herskowitz asked Tilghman.

"Not yet," Bill said, his ear against the door. "We'll wait until the first blow is struck."

Moments later the door burst open and the governor came out, his face livid. "That sonofabitch refuses to present me to the Grand Jury. I'll present myself, by God! Where's the jury room?"

"At the end of the hall," Bill said. "But . . ."

Without hearing the rest of the sentence, the governor

strode down the hall, flung open the last door and entered. When Tilghman caught up with him he was standing in the middle of an empty room.

"Where are they, Bill?"

"The jury has adjourned, Governor."

"When's it going to reconvene?"

"My guess is—not until you've left town."

"Damn! Damn!" He walked to the window and looked down. The mob saw him and a chorus of boos rose up. He turned and headed for the door. "I'm going down there and give that mob a piece of my mind."

Tilghman was standing in the doorway and though he didn't exactly block Robertson, he didn't move, either. "I wouldn't advise it, Governor."

"The hell you say!"

"You'd only inflame the mob, and it could be dangerous."

"What would you have me do? Sneak out of town with my tail between my legs?"

"No, sir, not that either. We have different plans. Waiting to meet you down there are four of the town's leading citizens—a doctor, a dentist and two merchants. They are going to shake your hand right there in front of the mob. These brave men are ready to make a public declaration against the Klan and it should have a very sobering effect on the crowd. These handshakes will accomplish more than any speech possibly could."

Robertson frowned, then sighed, then shrugged his shoulders. "I guess you're right, Bill. Let's go meet 'em."

As they walked together down the stairs, Tilghman said, "The important thing is not to show anger. If they boo you, grin and wave. Remember that the mob doesn't know what went on inside here; for all they know you may have control of the courthouse. When you step out, look happy, look triumphant."

"You ask a lot, Bill."

"I'm asking you to help me get you safely out of town."

"I'll do my best."

When they emerged from the building they were greeted by waves of boos. Standing on the top step, Robertson grinned broadly and waved to the crowd. He acted as if he were being cheered and this caused the boos to falter; the mob was momentarily confused. William Crume took Robertson by the arm and led him to a row of men standing on the top step, slightly to the right. The first to shake hands with the governor was a man named Horner, a State Senator. The next man in line was Ray Bool, a known Klansman. Crume was surprised but, thinking that Bool was coming over to their side, he introduced him to the governor. Robertson extended his hand but it was not taken. Bool spit on the steps, then said in a loud voice, "I'll not shake hands with a goddam thief."

With a boxer's fast reflexes, the governor slapped Bool's face with his left hand, followed up with a right to the jaw. Bool staggered back, was saved from falling by the men in line behind him. Regaining his balance, he leaped upon Robertson and the two of them wrestled on the narrow steps.

"Separate them, quick!" Tilghman snapped to Crume and Herskowitz, then ran down the steps.

When the first blow had landed, the mob cried out as if in pain. Then it became murmurous, shot through with whirls and eddies of unresolved emotion. Slowly it came together and began to flow in one direction—toward the two grappling men.

Tilghman had anticipated this and he stood on the bottom step, facing the mob. As the first wave of it came near, he put up a hand and said, "That's far enough." The front line stopped but the rear ones kept up the forward pressure. Tilghman spoke again. "I don't advise you to start any trouble."

The pressure of the rear ranks faltered, then subsided. At that moment, however, a strident voice came from behind Tilghman. It was the governor; he was giving his speech after all. He excoriated the mob, flayed it, damned it, goaded it, defied it. It listened sullenly, held in check by an immaculate and elderly man in a white hat. By what mystery was it done? Was he the stern father symbol? Or had he earned their respect by displaying a courage too noble to humble? No one knew, but there it was, a strange human chemistry that made one man stronger than a hundred.

When the governor finished his tirade, Tilghman led him from the steps to the waiting cars. Slowly the caravan drove through the crowd and out of town.

The Klan-dominated Grand Jury did later indict both Governor Robertson and Bill Tilghman, but they were never brought to trial. The hooded men knew what devastating witness Tilghman would make if he ever appeared in court, and they deemed it best to avoid giving him such a platform.

The problem of the Ku Klux Klan was to be with Oklahoma for a number of years but it had reached its peak that day in Okmulgee. After the confrontation with Governor Robertson and Marshal Tilghman it began a long, slow trip to obscurity, not to reappear until the great civil rights struggle four decades later.

29

John Walton succeeded Robertson as governor; Martin E. Trapp succeeded Walton. It made no difference who sat behind the big desk in Oklahoma City, Tilghman was the man sent for in times of trouble.

One of the most pressing problems facing Governor Trapp when he took office was the presence of convict work gangs on the capitol grounds. Walton had brought them there when he was governor, their job was to do landscape work. They had been installed in a wire-enclosed camp near the capitol grounds and were under constant police guard.

"The grapevine reports these men are planning a break," the governor said to Tilghman. "I'm worried."

"Do they have a grievance?"

"They think they do, I guess. When Walton brought them down here from prison he was supposed to have offered them pardons when they finished the job. I doubt it, but they *think* he pledged it, and they're angry at me for not following through on it. Hell, there are some hardened criminals out there; I can't turn them loose."

"Are the camp guards trustworthy?"

"That's another problem. The last legislature refused to appropriate money for their pay. They're working for nothing and they don't care what happens. If there is a break, they sure aren't going to risk their lives to stop it. And who can blame them? Bill, public safety demands that these men be returned to the penitentiary in McAlester. Will you undertake it?"

"I will."

Early the next morning Tilghman walked into the prison camp barracks and down the center aisle. Some of these men he had sent to prison, the others knew him by reputation. "Hi, Marshal," came greetings on all sides. He waved in response, then climbed on top of a table at the far end.

"Men," he called out, "you've finished your job here and I'm taking you back to prison tonight. You've done a good job, and it will be noted on your records for any future parole board hearings. Of course, if you cause any trouble, that will be noted on your records, too."

Several men rushed to look out the windows and saw that a company of National Guard had surrounded the barracks. One of the prisoners said bitterly, "We waited one day too long."

A railway car waited and the prisoners marched to it between rows of bayonet-wielding guardsmen under the command of Major Herskowitz. When they arrived in McAlester a fleet of buses was waiting to deliver them from the station to the penitentiary. That night every man was locked safely in his cell.

When Tilghman reported back, Governor Trapp grinned and said, "You used the National Guard. Hell, I could have done that."

"Sure, but you didn't."

"That's right, and I'm grateful, Bill. I have one more favor to ask of you. As you know, Walton was pretty lavish with paroles when he was governor, and a lot of them have been broken. I wish you'd track them down and return them to jail."

Tilghman undertook this "last" assignment, traveling over the prairie trails he knew so well. This time he traveled in a Ford instead of on horseback. After a couple of months he received a letter from the governor reporting that a number of legislators were complaining that he (Tilghman) was acting as judge and jury and decided which men to bring back to jail and which to let free. What did Tilghman have to say about these charges?

By way of answer Tilghman appeared in the governor's office with a man in patched overalls. Bill said, "This man has no influence, no one to speak for him. So I'll speak for him. There is all the evidence we need to extend his parole." Tilghman grabbed the man's wrists and held his hands out, palms up, for the governor to see. They were bent and callused from work in the cotton fields. "He went home to put in a crop so his wife and children would not starve."

"I understand," the governor said. "You keep on making the decisions, Bill."

It was a hot July day in 1924 and Bill Tilghman sat in a rocker on his front porch, fanning himself with a palmleaf fan. To his ears came the hum of bees and the strident sibilance of a cicada; to his nose the not unpleasant pungency of the stables; to his eyes the wind patterns drawn on a field of wheat. He was seventy and content with what he had done with his years.

He observed a dust cloud which announced an approaching car. It would be Zoe returning from town with the mail. She parked the car, came crisply up the steps to drop the mail in his lap, then continued on into the house. He glanced at a farm journal, a notice of a horse auction, several letters from old friends, and then he came upon a letter addressed in a hand he did not recognize. It was postmarked Cromwell, Okla. He didn't open the letter at once but ruminated, gathered together what he knew about Cromwell. There wasn't much. It was an oil boom town located about fifty miles southeast and, not unlike dozens of other towns that had sprung up in the rich oil fields, was ugly and temporary.

From his pocket he extracted a penknife and neatly cut the envelope open. He read the letter, frowning, then shifted in his chair and slowly read it a second time. When Zoe came out on the porch with a basket of mending he handed her the letter, which she read without change of expression.

"What are you going to do about it?" she finally asked.

"I don't rightly know. I gotta think about it."

She tried to formulate the best expression of her feelings. He was a stubborn man and a proud one; in twenty years of marriage she had certainly learned that. The phone rang before she could say what was on her mind. She went to answer it, then called out, "It's for you, Bill. Governor Trapp is calling."

"Hello, Governor," he said into the phone.

"Bill, you're going to get a letter from a citizens' committee in Cromwell . . ."

"I have it here."

"Oh. You made a decision?"

"No, sir, not yet."

"Well, that committee sent a couple of men up here to the capitol to see me. They want me to pressure you. I told them I wouldn't do it."

"I thank you for that."

"That's not to say I'm not worried about the situation," the governor added quickly, "and it doesn't mean I'm not in agreement with the folks in Cromwell that you're the best man in the country to take on their problem, but I told them I just couldn't pressure you, not after all you've done for Oklahoma. If there was ever a man who's laid his life on the line for the people of this territory and this state, it's Bill Tilghman. If there's a man who's earned a quiet retirement and a little peace and safety, it's Bill Tilghman. That's what I told them, and I wanted you to know, just in case they try to make out that I'm urging you. It's your decision, Bill."

"Thank you, Governor."

"But, Bill, if you do decide to go to Cromwell, you've got my full support. You know that."

"Yes, sir, I know that."

The phone went dead and Bill Tilghman returned to the front porch where he resumed rocking. Zoe had decided not to give her opinion until asked.

Around noon Fred Sutton stopped by to talk about a foal that had recently been born in Tilghman's stables. For the first time in Sutton's memory his old friend seemed uninterested in discussing horses. After a few minutes of desultory conversation, Tilghman thrust a letter into Sutton's hand and said, "What do you think about this?"

The letter was signed by W. E. Sirmans, who identified himself as secretary of the Cromwell Chamber of Commerce. It read, in part:

". . . I asked him [former U. S. Marshal E. D. Nix] if he thought it possible to get you to come down here and take charge of the situation and clean up this town . . . We have a boom town of 5000 people, with the usual hop peddlers, liquor joints, etc. . . . As soon as we started out the graft collectors realized that [our organization] would stop their money, so they set up a fight, and we found that the sheriff refused to commission any man we wanted . . . The businessmen of Cromwell realize they can do nothing unless they can secure a man like you, and a man that the sheriff of this county will not dare to refuse a commission to, to come here and take charge of things. All the businessmen will be back of you. I'm afraid the sheriff and the county attorney will not back us up. The gamblers pay $2500 each; each lodging house that has women, $40 a month—we have 31 of them . . . We also have a few hijackers here and we want to change their place of residence. We want you to come immediately, and if you will come, wire me you will come for $400 a month . . ."

Sutton finished the letter and said, "Bill, don't go."

"Why not?"

"Those aren't the kind of outlaws you know, not the old-time cowboy outlaw with some sort of code of honor. These are city-type gangsters brought about by Prohibition—bootleggers and pimps and dope peddlers. They'll shoot you in the back."

Tilghman looked thoughtful but unconvinced.

"Damn it, Bill," Sutton exclaimed, "you're seventy! You're not so quick on the draw as you were. And your eyesight is failing. It's time you realized you're an old man."

Zoe, standing just inside the open living room window, heard these words with dismay for she knew her husband's pride had been wounded. When he finally asked her advice, it would be too late, his mind would have been made up. She could tell by the way he squared his shoulders.

Leaving his family behind, Tilghman headed for Cromwell the following Monday.

30

The second day on the job in Cromwell Tilghman had a visit from Wiley Lynn. He entered the sheriff's small office to fill it with loud talk and the odor of pomade.

"Uncle Bill," he exclaimed, "welcome to Cromwell. I'm Wiley Lynn, Prohibition Enforcement Officer. Shake hands."

Tilghman was rather startled to hear himself called "Uncle Bill" by a stranger, but he shook hands as directed.

"Since we're the only officers in this town I thought we ought to get acquainted and help each other out if need be."

"I'm glad to have your cooperation, Mr. Lynn," Tilghman said. "I'll call on you if the need arises."

"Well, now," Lynn gave a carefully contrived chuckle, "what I meant was that if you find any bootleggers I'll handle them. That's as far as my authority goes. And do you know something, Uncle Bill? I'm glad. Bootleggers are reasonable men, but the murderers that infest this town, you can't trust them. Just as soon shoot you in the back as not. You know how many unsolved murders there's been in this town? Ten! Do you know why the murderers walk free? Because no bodies are ever found, no corpus delicti. I can tell you where some of them are. You know those big

round oil storage tanks? Well, sir, they're three stories tall
and each one holds 55,000 barrels of oil. There's a hatch
on the top of them and if a body is dropped in there it
won't be found until the tanks are cleaned out, which is
once in every three years. By the way, do you know what
happened to our last sheriff?"

"No, sir," Tilghman replied.

"Nobody knows, for sure, but I got a pretty good guess.
He's in one of those oil storage tanks. Next year, or the
year after, when they clean those tanks they'll find the
sheriff. Nobody's gonna be able to recognize him, but he'll
be there."

"Do you have any evidence . . ." Tilghman started to say.

"Nobody ever has any evidence in this town, and I guess
I'm like the others. I admit it, I'm no hero. I want to live
a few more years. So, you can hand the bootleggers over to
me, Uncle Bill, but don't expect me to go down a dark alley
to look for a gunman."

"I'll remember that," Tilghman said.

They shook hands again and Lynn left the office, trailing
his aroma of oily sweetness. Tilghman pondered on the significance of the visit just ended. Lynn's reference to bootleggers as "reasonable" men—was that a subtle offer of a bribe?
His announcement of the fate of the previous sheriff—was
that an attempt at intimidation? Or was the man simply a
fool?

Tilghman finally decided the latter was the case, and he
put Wiley Lynn out of his mind.

Over the following weeks Tilghman began to impose his
will on the town. The people began to feel safer (they even
stopped sleeping on roofs), more and more merchants
found the courage to speak out in his support. Tilghman
worked this change by a judicious mixture of firmness and
leniency; he did it by being inconspicuous until there was
the threat of trouble and then being very conspicuous; he
did it by obviously caring for the town and the people
who lived in it.

He ordered water barrels placed at every corner and organized a volunteer fire company to use them. He set a nine o'clock evening curfew for all women and children. He arranged for an itinerant preacher to make Cromwell a regular stop. He convinced one of the oil companies that it had a civic duty to convert one of its trucks into a community ambulance.

These changes were more surface than substance, however, and nobody knew this better than Tilghman. The decisive battle between law and anti-law was yet to occur.

During the second week of September Tilghman arrested a bootlegger with four cases of whiskey in his car, and took him to the county sheriff in Wewoka, there to be held until trial. Twenty-four hours later Tilghman saw the man walking into the movie house back in Cromwell. He immediately telephoned the sheriff at Wewoka and demanded an explanation.

"Sure I let him go," came the voice on the telephone. "I got a call from Wiley Lynn instructing me to do so. He said there wasn't enough evidence to hold him."

Slowly returning the receiver to its hook, Tilghman made a grimace. So, Lynn was the underworld fix, and probably the bagman, too. He now recalled several small events that pointed to this fact. He could not recall ever having so misjudged a man. He closed his eyes and for the first time felt the weight of his seventy years.

He roused himself and picked up the telephone, said into it, "Get me Joe Hagen in Slick." There was a long wait full of crackling sounds, but finally a voice came through.

"Sheriff Hagen," it said.

"Joe, this is Tilghman. You plan on being down my way any time soon?"

"Whenever you say, Marshal."

"How about this afternoon?"

"I'll start right out."

Joe Hagen, thirty-six-year-old sheriff of Okfuskee County and working out of Slick, Oklahoma, was part Pawnee In-

dian and idolized Tilghman. They had known each other
for many years, and Hagen had Tilghman's total trust.

Two hours after the phone conversation Hagen walked
in, a tall man slightly stooped and wearing an easy grin.
They shook hands briefly and Tilghman came directly to
the point.

"Yesterday I arrested a bootlegger and took him to
Wewoka. Had an airtight case on him. This morning he was
released on the orders of Wiley Lynn."

Hagen gave a silent whistle.

"Things are falling into shape. We knew they needed a
fixer, and their boldness indicated they had a good one.
Who could be better than a Federal officer?"

"Yeah, who better?" Hagen agreed.

"What I want to do now is review our narcotic problem in
the light of what we know about Lynn. Does his being the
fix man for the bootleggers change anything?"

"I don't think so. Cocaine has been coming into the area
very quietly, with no fuss at all. Because of this fact, we
had concluded that the bootleggers were also handling the
dope distribution. If there were two sets of distributors, one
for booze and another one for dope, there'd be some trouble.
I don't see how knowing about Lynn changes any of that."

"And Killian?"

Arnold Killian was a lease dealer, a sort of real estate
agent whose job was to find land that promised oil and
bring it to the attention of the drillers, all for a fee. Tilghman
had information that he was the brains behind the dope
ring. If so, he had the perfect cover job, for he could tour
all over the countryside any hour of the day or night without arousing suspicion.

"As I see it," Hagen said, "nothing's changed. I don't
figure Lynn bright enough to head the dope ring. He's probably the fix man for Killian, too."

"I agree," Tilghman said. Though no one else was in the
office, Tilghman lowered his voice. "Joe, another shipment
of cocaine is due the last week in October."

"By plane?"

"By plane from Mexico. The drop is to be made in a field out by the Amerada rig."

"You figure Killian to pick it up?"

"I don't figure him letting anybody else do it. We gotta catch him this go-round. There's not much time left."

The following day Tilghman hired a young man named Hugh Sawyer as deputy and, leaving him in charge, went home to Chandler for the weekend. Zoe was shocked at his appearance. The lines in his face had deepened and when he lowered himself into his rocking chair, he sighed from fatigue.

"Bill, when are you coming home to stay?" Zoe demanded.

"As soon as I finish my job," he said.

"That town is cleaned as much as it can be. Set a date for your retirement. I want you to set it right now."

"Other men will set that date, Zoe. But it will be soon."

"Soon! Soon!" she cried in exasperation. "Do you know what keeps you there? Stubborn pride. And that'll be what kills you . . . stubborn pride." She was near tears.

"Pride?" Tilghman said in a musing voice as he examined the thought. Then he quoted, " 'Though thou exalt thyself as the eagle, and though thou set thy nest among the stars, thence will I bring thee down, saith the Lord.' " He grinned at her and said, "Obadiah, Old Testament."

"I know my Bible," she snapped.

When Tilghman returned to Cromwell the following day he began to prepare for what he knew would be the showdown with Killian and Wiley Lynn. Win or lose, it would mark the end of his career. He had read too many symptoms of age in himself to continue on the job much longer. Zoe had charged him with pride, and perhaps she was right. He was proud of his name, his reputation, and he didn't want to do anything in the few remaining years that would tarnish work of a lifetime. He didn't want to hold the stage and the power too long, after his reflexes were slowed and his memory confused. He didn't want to be a museum piece, admired perhaps but laughed at behind his back. He damn well wanted the criminals to fear him, not patronize him. He didn't believe any of this had yet happened, but time was short. Smashing the narcotic ring would make for an appropriate exit, he thought, and he began to prepare for that fateful day.

On the afternoon of October 31 the phone on Tilghman's desk rang, and when he removed the receiver he recognized the voice of his informer. It said four words: "The drop is tonight." Then the line went dead. He immediately called a few trusted friends to his office and deputized them. There were Hugh Sawyer, his permanent deputy, W. E. Sirmans who was head of the committee that brought Tilghman to town in the first place, and Bill Curtis, manager of a casing crew that serviced many of the wells in the area.

Tilghman explained that they knew the field to which the dope would be flown but not the hour. They might have an all-night watch.

Sirmans asked, "Will the plane land or just fly over and drop the package?"

"I don't know," Tilghman said. "If it does land we must make certain to shoot out the tires so it can't take off."

"Are we certain that Killian will make the pickup?"

"We're not certain of anything. We have only the word of an informant. This whole thing might be a diversion pulling us to the south side of town while the delivery is made on the north side. We just don't know, and we can only play the cards dealt to us."

After dark that evening Tilghman and his men went on foot to the field and stationed themselves at opposite ends. If the plane arrived, and if Killian came to collect the dope, Tilghman and Sawyer would close in for the arrest while Sirmans and Curtis would cover them.

It was a dark night with scudding clouds blocking out the stars and giving only an occasional glimpse of a quarter moon. At ten-thirty they heard a sound that sent their hearts pounding, the sound of an airplane coming from the south, the direction of Mexico.

The clouds parted momentarily, sending a shaft of moonlight on the tiny biplane, a creature of cloth and wood and glue with an angry little engine. It swept over the field and then banked to come over a second time at treetop height. The pilot in the open cockpit shoved overboard a bulky package wrapped in white fabric and laced over and over with rope. He watched it fall to land in the center of the field, then put the plane into a steep climb and headed back south.

"That's it! That's it!" Sawyer whispered excitedly, slapping Tilghman on the back.

"Shhh," said Tilghman. "It's nothing in itself, no more important than a bundle of dirty laundry unless we catch Killian picking it up."

Again there was waiting and silence. Killian would come by car, Tilghman believed, and he kept looking down the single rutted road that led to the field. The last, distant, bee-sting sound of the airplane had faded away when a motor car approached from the north. Killian was known to own three cars—a Locomobile, a Stevens Duryea and a Pierce-Arrow—and Tilghman stared hard to identify the one now approaching. Its headlights were high and widely separated, molded out of the tops of the front fenders. This was a Pierce-Arrow.

The car stopped short of the field by fifty yards. It just stood there, motor running and lights on. No one got out of it. Then with a roar of power and a clash of gears, it turned around and raced back toward town.

"He spotted us," Sawyer said in amazement. "Somehow he spotted us!"

Tilghman said nothing. He was too bitterly disappointed to find the words.

3 I

Wiley Lynn awoke late in the morning and felt terrible. It was not only the hangover that had his head in a vise, but the memory of the dressing down he had received from Killian because of the failure of the narcotics drop. Killian seemed to blame him for Tilghman's presence at the field last night. It was the work of some goddam stoolie and how the hell was he supposed to know who the stoolie was?

With great effort he made it to a sitting position on the edge of the bed and stared at his fish-white feet while waiting for a surge of nausea to pass. When his stomach settled he resumed feeling sorry for himself. No one took him seriously, he decided. They seemed to think he could be ordered around like an errand boy. This day he'd show them!

After getting dressed he poured three ounces of corn liquor into a glass, drank it down, then went to Red's Cafe for breakfast. About noon he drove south out of town, headed for Wewoka. He had a date with Rose Lutke, madam of a brothel which had recently been closed down by the Wewoka sheriff. He had promised to help her find a new location for her business, possibly in Okemah where he had good connections. He was driving a Model T Ford touring car with Oklahoma license plates numbered 174-373.

When he arrived at Rose's house she had with her Eva Caton, who was also a madam, and a young man named David Thompson, an Army sergeant on leave.

"David here has never seen the oil fields," Rose explained. "Eva was gonna rent a car to show him the sights but I told her we was going to Okemah and they could ride along with us."

"All right," Lynn said indifferently.

"Well, ain't you the joy boy!" Rose exclaimed. "What the hell's wrong with you?"

"Nothing, goddam it."

"I sure don't look forward to spending a day with you in this mood. You got any whiskey?"

"Some corn in the back seat."

"Well, honey, let's pour some of that sunshine into you— right now!"

Several times during the trip Lynn drank from the half-gallon fruit jar, but it only served to darken his mood, make him more acutely aware of life's injustices. When they arrived at Okemah, Lynn and Rose went in to see the sheriff, leaving Eva and the sergeant in the car. They were in the sheriff's office for no more than ten minutes, and when they came back to the car Eva was teaching the sergeant some dirty songs.

"Can't you shut her up?" Lynn demanded.

"Seems a shame to," Rose said. "She's the only one having any fun."

"I got some business in Cromwell and I'd just as soon enter town quietly."

"Don't make such a fuss about everything. Another drink and she'll quiet down."

Rose was right. By the time they entered Cromwell that evening at ten o'clock, Eva had passed out in the back seat, the sergeant was barely conscious. Lynn drove the length of the main street, his eyes searching both sides of the road.

"Who you looking for?" Rose asked.

"A sonofabitch who thinks he's God," Lynn snarled.

Rose now became alarmed. "Wiley, don't start any trouble."

"Shut up," he snarled, threatening her with the back of his hand. Lynn parked the car across the street from Ma Murphy's dance hall. He said to Rose, "Let's see who's in Ma Murphy's."

They both got out of the car and started toward the dance hall. Halfway there Lynn pulled out his gun and shot it into the air. Startled, Rose backed toward the parked car. Lynn continued on.

Tilghman was inside the dance hall, having a cup of coffee at the snack bar. With him were Sirmans and Deputy Hugh Sawyer. They heard the shot and Tilghman slid off his stool and started for the door. He paused a moment when Hugh Sawyer took his arm.

"Bill, I'll go investigate," said the young man.

For just a moment Tilghman seemed to consider the offer, then he shook his head. "It's my job, Hugh. You can cover me."

As the door of the dance hall was pushed open the light spilled out to reveal Wiley Lynn standing on the edge of the boardwalk, gun in hand. Tilghman whipped out his own gun and in two quick steps closed with Lynn. His seventy-year-old reflexes were not as fast as they had once been but were still better than those of a man soaked in corn liquor. Tilghman grabbed Lynn's wrist and jerked it over his head so that the gun pointed harmless skyward, and at the same time jammed the barrel of his own gun hard into Lynn's ribs.

"Get his gun, Hugh," Tilghman called over his shoulder.

The deputy jumped forward to grab the gun and Tilghman released Lynn's arm. "You're drunk, Wiley. Go home and sleep it off."

"You sonofabitch," Lynn said thickly.

"Go on home." He took Lynn's arm to start him walking. "We'll talk tomorrow."

Jerking his arm free of Tilghman's grasp, Lynn snatched a second gun out of the waistband of his pants, fired three bullets into Tilghman's stomach.

With an expression of mild surprise and curiosity, Tilghman watched Lynn turn and sprint for his car. Tilghman started to say something but seemed to think better of it, for no words came. He closed his mouth, and then his eyes, and then he fell.

Deputy Sawyer emptied his gun at Lynn's car but with no apparent effect and it raced off into the night. This flurry of shots disrupted business as the curious came boiling out of the buildings and into the street. Gamblers left their cards, drinkers left their drinks, musicians put down their instruments and dancers stopped dancing, and they formed a large circle around the dead man. They were silent, not from reverence but disbelief.

Could such an uncommon man die in so mean a manner? Could this legendary man, this indestructible man, this giant of a man, could he be reduced to the crumpled body they saw in the dirt? If this was true, then no man was safe.

William Matthew Tilghman lay in state in the Capitol Building in Oklahoma City. "He died for the State he helped create," Governor Trapp said at the bier. "He set an example of modesty and courage that few could match, yet he made us all better men for the trying."

Services were held in the Presbyterian Church, then the funeral party accompanied the body to Chandler. The pallbearers were Governor Trapp, ex-Governor J. B. A. Robertson, Brigadier General Roy Hoffman, United States Marshal Alva McDonald, and two of Tilghman's old undersheriffs, G. W. Swanson and W. H. Crume.

Zoe Tilghman stood alone at the graveside. She was surrounded by her children and by the many notables, but she was alone with her grief. She recalled the words her husband had spoken his last weekend home. She had urged him to set the date for his retirement and he had said, "Other men will set that date." And so they had.

She wondered if she could have saved him. If she had insisted more strongly might he not have left Cromwell before it was too late? It was a question that would torment her for the rest of her life.

The minister spoke a brief prayer and then they lowered Bill Tilghman into his grave, into the earth on which he had so often slept.

After the graveside service was ended, William Sirmans took Joe Hagen aside and said, "Cromwell needs a new town marshal, and quick. Do you have any opinions who it should be?"

Hagen whistled soundlessly. "There's not a man in the entire country who can sit on the lid at Cromwell the way Bill Tilghman did."

"Perhaps not, but we have to have a marshal who'll try."

"How about Bill's deputy, Hugh Sawyer?"

"Too young and too hot-headed. He blames himself for Tilghman's death and he's out to even the account. He needs to be controlled by an older and more experienced officer. Our committee has given this problem a lot of study, Joe, and we unanimously agree that you're the man for the job. Don't give me an answer until you've thought it over. The way I see it, you owe it to Bill's memory not to let all his work go in vain. That may sound like I'm putting the arm on you, and I guess I am."

On the night of the murder Wiley Lynn had raced southward on the back roads to escape the lynch mob he was certain had formed in Cromwell. When he left Seminole County and entered Hughes County he felt no safer. Though no mob was after him, the thought became an obsession and the next day he surrendered himself in Holdenville where there was a strong jail.

The trial of Wiley Lynn for murder opened on May 21, 1925, at Wewoka and was presided over by District Judge Frank Matthews. The courtroom was packed with specta-

tors, most of whom had brought their lunches in paper
sacks. They had come for a Roman Holiday, and were not to
be disappointed.

The prosecution would have normally been handled by
the county attorney and his assistant (Walter Billingsley
and Homer Bishop), but there was too much political hay
to be made out of this trial and Billingsley found himself
receiving rather unwelcome assistance from big shots down
from Oklahoma City.

Seated at the prosecution table in court were: Prince
Freeling, former Oklahoma Attorney General, known as the
"man with the golden voice"; the current Attorney General
for the State, Edwin Dabney; General Roy Hoffman, and,
squeezed to the far end of the table, Billingsley and Bishop.

In dramatic contrast, the defense table held only Wiley
Lynn and his one attorney, W. W. Pryor, known as "the
Clarence Darrow of the West." This David and Goliath
setting was not lost on the jury of farmers and oil workers.
During his opening speech, Pryor made sure the jury got
the point by naming off each member of the prosecution
staff and using his title "General." Then he said to the jury,
"The fact that all these generals are against my client,
would that prejudice you against him?"

Indeed it would not!

Throughout the trial the distinguished prosecutors vied
with each other to get the floor and make orations. Pryor
was content to build his case quietly, brick by brick:

1. Wiley Lynn was a Federal officer and legally carried firearms.

2. He had reason to believe that Ma Murphy was
selling bootleg and it was his duty to search her place
and confiscate the liquor.

3. As he approached her dance hall he tried to put
the safety on his gun and it had accidentally discharged.

4. Tilghman, known to be a friend of Ma Murphy's,
tried to prevent Lynn from entering the premises and
doing his duty.

5. When Tilghman put his gun in Lynn's ribs, Lynn
thought he was about to be murdered. Therefore, Lynn
fired in self-defense.

In his instructions to the jury, Judge Matthews said, in
part ". . . It is not necessary to the right of self-defense
that the danger should in fact exist . . . The person threatened with such apparent danger has the same right to de-
fend against it . . . [as] he would have were the danger
real."

The jury's verdict was that Wiley Lynn acted in self-
defense and was therefore innocent of murder.

The acquittal of Wiley Lynn caused dismay throughout
the state, but rough justice was soon to be done. On a Sunday afternoon in a crowded ice cream parlor in Madill,
Oklahoma, Lynn opened fire on Crockett Long, a state policeman who had once arrested him. Long drew his gun
and when the exchange of shots ended, both men were
dead, as was seventeen-year-old Rody Watkins, a farm boy
who took a ricochet bullet in his heart.

Joe Hagen accepted the marshal's job in Cromwell and
to his amazement, found he had rather little to do. A strange
metamorphosis had taken place in the town. When Tilghman had been gunned down, the people responded with
both anger and fear. It was a disaster—no less than flood
or fire—and they came together to comfort and help each
other. When they saw how many they were, they stopped
being frightened, they felt their power and they turned on
the grafters and drove them out of town.

"They did it for Bill Tilghman as much as for themselves,"
Hagen remarked to Sirmans one day. "Bill cleaned up this
town from his grave. I never saw that happen before. I
don't suppose I ever will again."

One Man with courage makes a majority.
    —*Andrew Jackson*

BIBLIOGRAPHY

Adams, Ramon F. *Six-Guns and Saddle Leather*. Bibliography, University of Oklahoma Press, Norman, Okla. 1954

Aikman, Duncan. *Calamity Jane and the Lady Wildcats*. Henry Holt & Co., New York, 1927

American Scene. Oklahoma Issue. Vol. IV, #4, Gilcrease Institute, Tulsa, Okla., 1962

Barnard, Evan. *A Rider of the Cherokee Strip*. Houghton Mifflin Co., Boston, 1936

Beadles, John. *Western Wilds and the Men Who Redeemed Them*. Jones Brothers & Co., Cincinnati, Ohio, 1878

Beebe, Lucius M., and Clegg, Charles. *Hear the Train Blow*. E. P. Dutton & Co., New York, 1952

Botkin, B. A. *A Treasury of Western Folklore*. Crown, New York, 1951

Bradley, Glenn D. *The Story of the Santa Fe*. Richard G. Badger, Boston, Mass., 1920

Breehan, Carl. *Badmen of the Frontier Days*. Robert McBride Co., New York, 1957

Canton, Frank. *Frontier Trails*. Houghton Mifflin Co., Boston, 1930

Carey, Henry L. *The Thrill Story of Famous Boot Hill and Modern Dodge City*. Herbert Etrick, Dodge City, 1937

Casey, Robert. *The Black Hills*. Bobbs-Merrill Co., Indianapolis, Ind., 1949

Chapel, Charles Edward. *Guns of the Old West.* Coward-McCann, New York, 1961

Chapman, B. B. *The Founding of Stillwater.* Times Journal Publishing Company, Oklahoma City, 1948

Chisholm, Joe. *Brewery Gulch.* Naylor Co., San Antonio, Texas, 1949

Clark, Ira G. *Then Came the Railroads.* University of Oklahoma Press, Norman, Okla., 1958

Croy, Homer. *We Hanged Them High.* Little, Brown & Co., Boston, 1952

Crumbine, Samuel J. *Frontier Doctor.* Dorrance & Co., Philadelphia, 1948

Cunningham, Eugene. *Triggernometry.* Caxton Printers, Caldwell, Idaho, 1941

Dalton Brothers. *The Dalton Brothers.* Laird & Lee, Chicago, 1892

Dalton, Emmett. *When the Daltons Rode.* Doubleday, Doran & Co., Garden City, N.Y., 1931

Davis, Clyde. *The Arkansas.* Farrar & Rhinehart, New York, 1940

Debo, Angie. *The Cowman's Southwest.* Arthur H. Clark Co., Glendale, Calif., 1953

Dick, Everett. *The Sod-House Frontier.* Appleton-Century Co., New York, 1937

Dobie, J. Frank. *Southwestern Lore.* Texas Folklore Society, Vol. IX, Southwest Press, Dallas, 1931

Dunn, J. P. *Massacres of the Mountains.* Archer House, New York, 1965

Elliott, David. *Last Raid of the Daltons.* Coffeyville Journal, Coffeyville, Okla., 1892

Ewers, John. *Artists of the Old West.* Doubleday & Co., New York, 1965

Fast, Howard. *The Last Frontier.* Duell, Sloan & Pearce, New York, 1942

Foy, Eddie. *Clowning Through Life.* E. P. Dutton & Co., New York, 1928

Gard, Wayne. *Frontier Justice.* University of Oklahoma Press, Norman, Okla., 1949

Graves, Richard. *Oklahoma Outlaws.* State Printing Company, Oklahoma City, Okla., 1915

Gunther, John. *Inside U.S.A.* Harper & Brothers, New York, 1947

Harman, S. W. *Hell on the Border.* Phoenix Publishing Co., Fort Smith, Ark., 1898

Harrington, Fred. *Hanging Judge.* Caxton Printers, Caldwell, Idaho, 1951

Hendricks, George. *The Bad Men of the West.* The Naylor Co., San Antonio, Texas, 1942

Horan, James. *Desperate Women.* G. P. Putnam's Sons, New York, 1952

Houts, Marshall. *From Gun to Gavel.* Wm. Morrow & Co., New York, 1954

James, Marquis. *They Had Their Hour.* Bobbs-Merrill Co., Indianapolis, Ind., 1934

Jones, W. F. *The Experiences of a Deputy U. S. Marshal of the Indian Territory.* W. F. Jones, Tulsa, Okla., 1937

King, Frank. *Mavericks.* Trail's End Publishing Co., Pasadena, Calif., 1947

Lewis, Alfred. *The Sunset Trail.* A. S. Barnes & Co., New York, 1905

Ludlum, Stewart. *Great Shooting Stories.* Doubleday & Co., New York, 1947

McDade, Thomas. *The Annals of Murder.* University of Oklahoma Press, Norman, Okla., 1961

McReynolds, Robert. *Thirty Years on the Frontier.* El Paso Publishing Co., Colorado Springs, 1906

McRill, Albert. *And Satan Came Also.* Britton Publishing Co., Oklahoma City, 1955

Marshall, James. *Santa Fe.* Random House, New York, 1945

Morris, Lerona Rosamond. *Oklahoma Yesterday-Today-and Tomorrow.* Coop Publishing Co., Guthrie, Okla., 1932

Newsom, J. A. *The Life and Practice of the Wild and Modern Indian.* Harlow Publishing Co., Oklahoma City, 1923
Nix, Evett, and Hines, Gordon. *Oklahombres.* Eden Publishing House, St. Louis-Chicago, 1929

Oklahoma, Chronicles of. Volumes 2, 9, 10, 18, 24, 26, 31, 36
Oklahoma, Past and Present. Frontier Publishing Co., Oklahoma City, 1940

Pinkerton, William. *Train Robberies.* International Association of Chiefs of Police, Jamestown, Va., 1907
Preece, Harold. *The Dalton Gang.* Hastings House, New York, 1963
—— *Living Pioneers.* World Publishing Co., Cleveland, Ohio, 1952

Raine, William. *Guns of the Frontier.* Houghton Mifflin, Boston, 1940
Rainey, George. *The Cherokee Strip.* Enid, Okla., 1925
Riegel, George. *America Moves West.* Henry Holt & Co., New York, 1930
Rister, Carl. *Oil! Titan of the Southwest.* University of Oklahoma Press, Norman, Okla.
—— *No Man's Land.* University of Oklahoma Press, Norman, Okla., 1948

Sabin, Edwin. *Wild Men of the Wild West.* Thomas Y. Crowell, New York, 1929
Shirley, Glenn. *Toughest of Them All.* University of New Mexico Press, Albuquerque, N.M., 1953
—— *Law West of Fort Smith.* Henry Holt & Co., New York, 1957
—— *Six Guns and Silver Star.* University of New Mexico Press, Albuquerque, N.M., 1958
—— *Heck Thomas, Frontier Marshal.* Chilton Books, Philadelphia, 1962

—— *Henry Starr, Last of the Real Badmen.* David McKay Company, New York, 1965

Sutton, Fred. *Hands Up.* Bobbs-Merrill, Indianapolis, Ind., 1927

Thomas, George. *Bat Masterson.* Kansas State Printing Plant, Topeka, Kan., 1943

Tilghman, Zoe. *Quarter Horses and Racing in the Southwest.* Kansas Historical Collection, Vol. XVIII, p. 348

—— *Outlaw Days.* Harlow Publishing Co., Oklahoma City, 1926

—— *Quanah, The Eagle of the Commanches.* Harlow Publishing Co., Oklahoma City, 1938

—— *Marshal of the Last Frontier.* Arthur H. Clark Company, Glendale, Calif., 1949

Vestal, Stanley. *Short Grass Country.* Duell, Sloane & Pearce, New York, 1941

—— *Queen of the Cow Towns—Dodge City.* Harper & Brothers, New York, 1952

—— *Why the West Was Wild.* Kansas State Historical Society. Topeka, Kan., 1963

Wright, Muriel. *The Story of Oklahoma.* Webb Publishing Co., Oklahoma City, 1930

Writers of the Works Progress Administration. *Oklahoma—a Guide to the Sooner State.* University of Oklahoma Press, Norman, Okla., 1941

INDEX